Level 3

Health and Social Care
Principles and Contexts

CW00672381

wjec cbac | City & Guilds

Carol Bennett

Sara Jones

Rhiannon Salisbury

Philip Webber

Level 3 Health and Social Care: Principles and Contexts

Ariennir yn Rhannol gan
Lywodraeth Cymru
Part Funded by
Welsh Government

Published under the sponsorship of WJEC's Teaching and Learning Resources Scheme

Published by CAA Cymru, Fagwyr Buildings, Llanfihangel Genau'r Glyn, Aberystwyth, Ceredigion SY24 5AQ

First published in 2024 by CAA Cymru – an Atebol brand

Copyright © WJEC 2024

ISBN 978-1-80106-442-2

All rights reserved

Subject consultants: Amanda Jones and Dr Angharad Jones, Healthcare Education Centre, Aberystwyth University
Editing and Proofreading: Glyn Saunders Jones and Helen Lowcock James
Copyright: Sion Saunders-Jones
Designed by Owain Hammonds

The use of the name City & Guilds and the City & Guilds logo are copyrighted trademarks of The City and Guilds of London Institute. City & Guilds Logo © City & Guilds 2024

Cover photo: iStock
Printed and bound in Wales

A catalogue record for this publication is available from the National Library of Wales and the British Library.

Although every effort has been made to ensure that website addresses are correct at the time of printing, CAA Cymru/Atebol cannot be held responsible for the content of any website mentioned in this book. It is sometimes possible to find a web page that has been relocated by typing the homepage address for a website into your browser's URL window.

CAA Cymru's policy is to use paper that is a natural, renewable and recyclable product made from trees grown in well-managed forests and other controlled sources. The felling of the trees and the subsequent steps are expected to comply with the environmental regulations of the country of origin.

Contents

Introduction

This book is designed to support learners studying the WJEC and City & Guilds Level 3 Health and Social Care: Principles and Contexts qualifications. This qualification has been designed for post-16 learners who are interested in learning more about the health and social care sectors in Wales and beyond.

This qualification will provide you with a suitable progression route for those of you who have studied Level 2 qualifications within the health and social care, and childcare qualifications including:

- Level 2 Health and social Care: Principles and Contexts
- GCSE Health and Social Care, and Childcare
- Level 2 Health and Social Care: Core, or
- Level 2 children's Care, Play Learning and Development: Core.

This qualification is also suitable for learners who have not previously studied Health and Social Care, but who are capable of Level 3 study. People who undertake this qualification may be in school or college and thinking about starting a career in health and social care, or they may be already in a job, starting a new career or, have worked in the Health and Social Care for a long time. Whatever your situation, this book is for you!

Working in health and social care, whether supporting children and young people or adults, requires a great deal of skills and knowledge, which you will continue to develop throughout your career. This qualification will enable you to develop and demonstrate knowledge, skills and understanding within the context of health and social care services. The knowledge, understanding and skills you are required to achieve within this qualification, build on the content of the Health and Social Care: Core qualification. It is a requirement of Social Care Wales that an individual working within the Health and Social Care sector will need the Core qualification, and a relevant Practice qualification to work within specific job roles.

This qualification will provide you with a suitable foundation for the study of health and social care through a range of higher education courses, or apprenticeships. You may also progress to other qualifications within the health and social care and childcare qualifications, for example the Level 2 and Level 3 Health and Social Care Practice qualifications. This will provide you with a great foundation to support your work, so that you can move on to further learning and development in the future.

The aim of this qualification is to enable you to develop knowledge and an understanding of:

- the principles and values of Health and Social Care practice and how to apply them to a range of health and social care contexts

- reflective practices and the ways in which individuals' unique needs can be identified and responded to

- ways in which effective, person-centred practice and well-being within health and social care can be promoted and supported

- how to analyse, interpret and evaluate theories in health and social care, and an opportunity to reflect on how they could influence practice

- changing sector policy, and how these changes affect service development and delivery.

You will also be required to undertake non-examination assessments (NEA). These contain tasks set by WJEC, which will require you to draw on your knowledge and understanding to complete the tasks. You should have plenty of time and support to help you to prepare for these assessments.

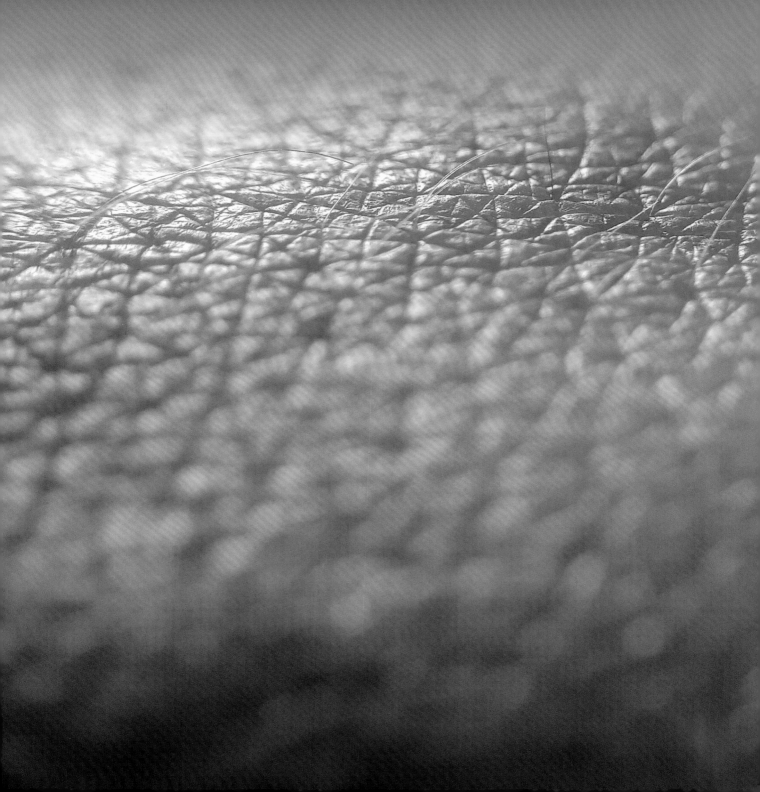

Unit 4

Understanding how the human body is affected by common conditions

Unit 4: Introduction

Understanding how the human body is affected by common conditions

Overview

In this unit, you will gain knowledge and understanding of the types and causes of common conditions, and you will investigate how they can affect the human body. You will also examine the care and support available to individuals living with physiological conditions, and the challenges they may face when living with the effects of common conditions.

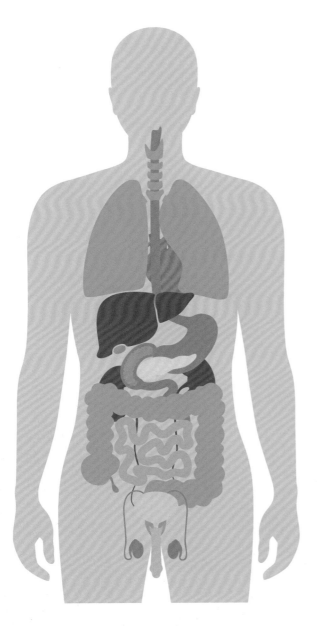

Assessment

This unit is internally assessed through one set assignment: writing an article and producing an infographic on a specific infectious and physiological condition for a health and social care magazine.

You will spend 15 hours in total producing the evidence for this assessment, completing the work under supervised conditions. The assignment is based on a set task and accompanying stimuli; the stimulus for this non-examination assessment (NEA) will change each year.

The task is based on two pieces of stimuli which will be included in the assessment pack, available to centres from the WJEC secure website on the first Monday in September each year. The tasks for this non-examination assessment will remain the same for the lifetime of the specification, as published in the Assessment Pack available from the WJEC secure website.

The conditions listed within the WJEC specification are examples of common conditions that occur in Wales. The list of conditions in the specification is not exhaustive, and the stimuli released for the NEA may include other common conditions that occur in Wales.

Sample Assessment Materials
(Internal Non-Exam Assessment (NEA))

Task 1

You have been asked to write an article and produce an infographic on specific infectious and physiological conditions for a health and social care magazine. Your article must relate to the physiological condition in stimulus 1 and your infographic must relate to the infection in stimulus 2.

You should spend 15 hours on this task. The maximum word count for this task is 3,000 (including the infographic). You may use the following resources when completing this task:

- ICT software
- Stimuli. Class notes can be used. These should consist of a maximum of six sides of A4 paper. They may be handwritten or word processed. They should be in the candidate's own words and should not include pre-written answers. The teacher/assessor is responsible for reviewing the notes to ensure they are within the guidance above. All notes used by the candidate must be retained by the centre.

You are allowed to access the internet whilst completing this task. Sample Assessment Material stimuli:

Stimulus 1:

Physiological condition – Type 2 Diabetes: More than 200,000 people in Wales, approximately 7% of the population, are known to have a form of diabetes (including about 16,000 cases of type 1 diabetes). It is estimated that a further 61,000 people are yet to be diagnosed with type 2 diabetes and 350,000 people are thought to be at high risk of developing type 2 diabetes. According to recent data from Diabetes UK Cymru, 7.4% of the population have diabetes, compared to the UK average of 6.8%. The total number of people living in Wales with diabetes is therefore about 256,000. Public Health Wales (PHW) says around 60% of adults in Wales are overweight or obese. Although not every case of type 2 diabetes is caused by excessive weight, it is the single greatest risk factor for developing the condition. Age, family history, and ethnicity can also contribute to someone's risk. Many cases of type 2 diabetes could be prevented or delayed by healthy eating, being more active, and maintaining a healthy weight. Diabetes UK Cymru said spotting the early signs of diabetes can be life-changing.

Source: Diabetes UK Cymru

Stimulus 2:

Infectious condition – Tuberculosis (TB) outbreak: In May 2019 at Llwynhendy in Carmarthenshire there was an outbreak of tuberculosis. Following the death of one person, the local residents were offered screening for the disease. The screening showed that 29 people had the infection, and that an additional 80 cases had been identified as contacts of confirmed cases. Public Health Wales (PHW) said that there was a strong possibility of additional cases being identified at a later date. They then contacted people who had been in contact with confirmed cases, as there could be a possibility that screening could bring to light more cases that had not been identified earlier. Screening would enable more tests to be held, followed by treatment if required. Dr Brendan Mason, from PHW, said community screening was the "best course of action in order to bring this outbreak under control". He said that the outbreak of tuberculosis also coincided with a shift in global health strategies focused on eradicating the disease by 2035.

Source: Public Health Wales 2019

Your article must:

With reference to stimulus 1

(a) Explain the possible causes and effects of the condition referred to in the stimulus. Your answer must refer to:

- possible causes of the condition

- signs and symptoms

- short-term effects on the human body

- long-term effects on the human body

- impact on daily living.

[22 marks]

(b) Describe the types of risk reduction strategies that can be implemented to support the health and well-being of individuals living with the condition referred to in the stimulus.   **[10 marks]**

(c) Assess the type of care and support individuals, their family, friends and wider circle may need when living with the condition referred to in the stimulus. Your response should include reference to relevant models of health and well-being.   **[18 marks]**

With reference to stimulus 2

(d) Produce an infographic outlining your understanding of the infection in stimulus 2. Your infographic must include reference to:

- the type of infection

- how the infection is caused

- the transmission cycle for the infection, including how it enters the body

- any long-term damage that may occur as a result of the infection.

[10 marks]

TOTAL MARKS: 60 marks

All content may be assessed through any of the assessment objectives (AOs):

Assessment objective	% of allocated marks
AO1 – Demonstrate knowledge and understanding of a range of key concepts, values, and issues that are related to health and social care.	30-34%
AO2 – Apply knowledge and understanding of health and social care principles and contexts.	33-37%
AO3 – Analyse and evaluate health and social care theories and practice to demonstrate understanding, reflecting on how they can influence	31-35%

Areas of content

When studying Unit 4, you may be assessed on all five areas of content. Within this section of the textbook, there are five chapters covering some aspects of the content.

Chapter	Areas of content
Chapter 1	4.1 Types and causes of infection, ways infections are transmitted and resulting conditions
Chapter 2	4.2 The causes and effects of a range of physiological conditions
Chapter 3	4.3 How the human body is affected by common conditions
Chapter 4	4.4 Care and support when living with physiological conditions and challenges
Chapter 5	4.5 Risk reduction strategies that can be implemented to support health and well-being

4.1: Types and causes of infection, ways infections are transmitted and resulting conditions

What is an infection?

It is important to know and understand that:

- An infection is an invasion of body tissues by a foreign organism, and there are several different types of infection

- The different types of infections and the symptoms of an infection depend on the organism responsible and the site of infection

- There is a **transmission** cycle for infections and how they enter the body

An infection can be defined as an attack on the body, or part of the body, by **microorganisms** that thrive on causing potential harm. These infection-causing microorganisms are called pathogens or infectious agents.

In 2018, the World Health Organisation cited infectious diseases among the top 10 causes of death worldwide. Infections included as the leading causes of death are respiratory infections, diarrhoeal diseases and tuberculosis. In some countries, infections of the respiratory system and diseases causing diarrhoea are the top two causes of death. In the UK, between 1915 and 1945, people were dying in large numbers from infections, but by 2015, the

Key terms

Communicable condition: a condition that can be passed from one individual to another.

Non-communicable condition: is not transferable directly from one individual to another.

Condition/disease: causes changes to the body's normal functioning, leading to specific symptoms and challenges.

Infectious condition: a condition caused by a microorganism; it may or may not be a communicable condition.

Microorganisms: exist everywhere, including on body surfaces, such as on the skin, in the digestive system, and other areas that are open to the outside world (such as the mouth, upper respiratory system, the reproductive tract, and urinary tract); most microorganisms do not cause harm to the human body, and some are even beneficial.

Transmission: is the process where an infection may be passed on from human to human, animal to human, or the environment to human.

Acute infections: result in a sudden or rapid onset of disease which only lasts a short time, such as influenza.

Chronic infections: have a prolonged incubation period followed by progressive disease such as cancer, which may last for months or years.

most common causes of death were cancer, heart conditions or other causes. There was a decline in the number of people dying from infectious diseases in the 20th century. Infections such as poliomyelitis (polio), diphtheria, tetanus, whooping cough, measles, mumps, and rubella were more or less eradicated by the second half of the 20th century, after childhood immunisation was introduced.

Infectious agents differ in how they cause changes to the function of the human body. If the **pathogen** produces no evidence of changes to the body, it is asymptomatic (not causing symptoms). However, a noticeable difference in the body's normal functioning or part of the body is referred to as a disease.

Pathogens also vary in the severity of the diseases they produce and how they are transmitted (passed on). If the pathogen can be transmitted from one individual to another, the resulting condition is a communicable disease.

Many pathogens that are usually harmless can cause an infection under certain circumstances. Most pathogens will cause an infection in any healthy individual; however, an opportunistic pathogen will cause disease only in a susceptible individual (an individual whose immune system mechanism for fighting the pathogen is low).

An infection generally develops into a disease when the signs and symptoms of the infection are distinctive and can be differentiated from other conditions.

Key terms

Localised/systemic infections: affect only one body part or organ, such as urinary bladder infections. Severe systematic infections may have life-threatening effects, such as sepsis or septic shock.

Pathogens: are organisms causing disease such as bacteria (e.g. food poisoning), fungi (e.g. athlete's foot), viruses (e.g. influenza), protozoa (e.g. malaria) and parasites (e.g. lice infestation).

Resident flora: Microbes found permanently in a specific body site.

NB. You need to know about the different types of infections. The symptoms of an infection are dependent on the organism that has caused the infection and also the site of the infection.

Common types and causes of infections:

Prion infections: are transmissible, untreatable and fatal brain diseases, such as Creutzfeldt-Jakob Disease (CJD) and neurodegenerative disease.

Healthcare-associated infections (HCAIs): develop within a healthcare environment such as a hospital, and have been caused by interventions

(medical/surgical treatment) or contact within the setting such as MRSA (Methicillin-Resistant Staphylococcus Aureus).

Bacterial infections e.g. Lyme disease, meningitis and pneumonia.

Fungal infections e.g. ring worm, athlete's foot and keratitis eye infection.

Parasitic infections e.g. thread worms, mites and lice.

Viral infections e.g. influenza, chicken pox and glandular fever.

Protozoal infections e.g. malaria and toxoplasmosis.

Types of infection

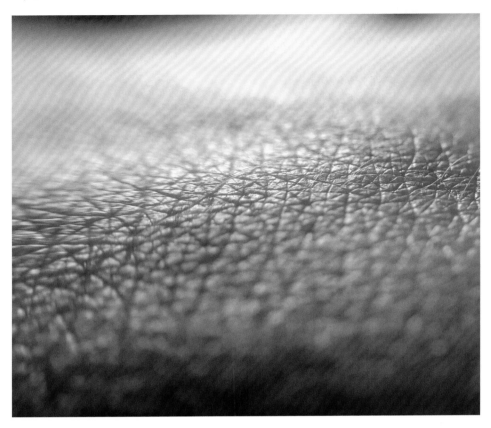

Colonisation

Colonisation is a process by which strains of microorganisms grow and live on or in the body, in areas such as the skin, nose, mouth, throat, large intestine, and vagina. The microorganisms usually found on a particular area of the body are called the resident flora, and may grow and replicate, but do not cause disease. An infection will occur when a new or resident microorganism invades a part of the body where the usual defence mechanism is ineffective. The pathogen causes a change in the body's functioning.

Systemic infection

A systemic infection can be caused by viruses or bacteria which spread throughout the systems of the body. The common signs and symptoms of a systemic infection may include fever and chills, abnormal body temperature, rapid pulse, and rapid breathing.

Systemic infections are not always more severe than localised infections, although they affect a more significant proportion of the body. Systemic **bacterial infections** may be referred to as sepsis; it is not a **communicable condition**; however, the pathogens that cause sepsis are usually contagious.

Localised infection

A **localised infection** is usually caused by bacteria or viruses where the symptoms are localised in one area, i.e. in one specific area of the body. The common signs and symptoms of a localised infection may include heat, swelling, pain (in the affected area), and redness.

Acute and chronic infections

- **Acute infections** usually appear suddenly or last a short amount of time.
- **Chronic infections** may occur slowly over an extended period and may last for months or years.

Healthcare Associated Infections (HCAIs)

Healthcare associated infections (HCAIs) are known as infections associated with the delivery of healthcare services in a healthcare environment. HCAIs are caused either due to healthcare interventions, such as medical or surgical treatment, or due to contact within a healthcare setting. The most common sites in the human body for HCAIs are the urinary tract, the respiratory tract, the bloodstream and wounds. The microorganisms that cause HCAIs can originate from the **resident flora** of the patient themselves, or from the hospital environment and hospital workers. Medical staff will need to identify the patients who are most at risk to HCAIs. These risks can include the very young, premature babies and young children who are seriously ill. Others that are more susceptible to risk of infection include the frail and elderly with specific medical conditions such as diabetes or a chest condition. People receiving cancer treatments such as chemotherapy will also have a weakened immune system, and are therefore at a greater risk of infection.

Factors that contribute toward the development of HCAIs:

- the individual's normal defences against infection are lowered by surgery or illness.
- hands of healthcare workers are a common vehicle for the spread of microorganisms; insufficient handwashing is an essential factor contributing to the spread of HCAIs.

The cost of HCAIs to the patient, staffing in healthcare settings and the NHS is significant. HCAIs extend hospital stays, increase the time patients are away from work, cause disability and discomfort, and even result in loss of life.

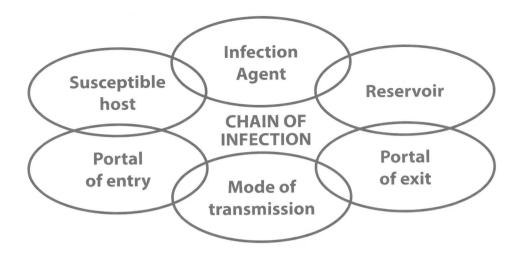

The transmission cycle for infection

The transmission cycle for infections can be described as a chain consisting of six links:

- the infectious agent
- a reservoir
- a portal of exit
- a mode of transmission
- a portal of entry
- a susceptible host.

1. Infectious agent – This is the microorganism or the pathogens that cause the infection (bacteria, virus, fungi, protozoa, parasite, or prion).

2. Reservoir – The source of the infection or the environment in which the microorganism typically lives and where it will grow. Reservoirs of infection involve humans, animals, and the environment. Many common infectious diseases have human reservoirs that may or may not show the effects of illness.

A *carrier* is a person who does not show signs of infection but can transmit the pathogen to others; asymptomatic or healthy carriers are individuals who do not experience symptoms despite being infected.

- Incubatory carriers are individuals who can transmit the pathogen during the incubation period before the signs of infection begin.

- Convalescent carriers are individuals who have recovered from the infection but remain capable of transmitting to others.

- Chronic carriers are individuals who continue to be a reservoir for a pathogen for months, or even years, after their initial infection.

3. Portal of exit – This is the route by which the infectious organism can escape from the reservoir. Before an infection is transmitted to a new host, the microorganism must leave the reservoir.

4. Mode of transmission – This is the link between the source of the infection (reservoir) and the portal of entry. After a microorganism leaves its source or reservoir, it requires a mode of transmission to reach another person. There are three primary modes of transmission:

- Direct transmission: involves direct transfer of the microorganism from person-to-person through touching, including kissing and sexual intercourse. Spread from droplets is also a form of direct transmission, but can only occur if the source or the host are within a few metres of each other; sneezing, coughing, spitting, talking, or singing can spread droplets onto the eyes, nose, or mouth of another person.

- Indirect transmission: vehicle-borne – a vehicle is any material that provides an 'in-between' means to transport and introduce an infectious agent into another person through a suitable portal of entry. Fomites (non-living materials or objects) such as toys, tissues, soiled clothes, eating or cooking utensils, surgical instruments, and wound dressings can act as vehicles for transmission.

- Indirect transmission: vector-borne transmission – a vector is an animal or insect that provides an 'in-between' means of transporting the infectious agent. Transmission may occur by when the insect injects its saliva during biting of the skin, or when an animal bites or deposits faeces or other materials on the skin or wound.

You need to know and understand how microorganisms enter the human body, to include:

- Air-borne transmission: may involve the transmission of the infectious agent through droplets or dust. Evaporated droplets produced by a cough or sneeze of an infected person can remain in the air for long periods. Dust particles containing an infectious agent can also become air-borne and be passed by air to another person.

- Water-borne transmission and ingestion: microorganisms capable of causing disease (pathogens) enter the body through the mouth from contaminated food or drinks and enter the digestive system. Microorganisms, such E.coli and salmonella enter the digestive system in this manner.

- Transmission through body fluids such as blood, semen, vaginal secretions, discharge from wounds and saliva: can transmit communicable diseases such as hepatitis B, Hepatitis C and human immune deficiency virus HIV/AIDS.

5. Portal of entry – The infectious agent enters the individual (the host). The skin is usually a barrier to infectious agents. However, any break in the skin will provide a portal of entry for the infectious agent. Microorganisms often enter the body of a host in the same way they used to leave the source.

Activity

At one time, smallpox was a common infectious disease, caused by the variola virus, and was estimated to be responsible for between 300 million and 500 million deaths worldwide. The last naturally occurring case of smallpox was in 1977, and the World Health Organization (WHO) went on to certify the eradication of smallpox globally in 1980. This was made possible by creating a smallpox vaccine in 1796, the first successful vaccine to be developed.

Q. Which part of the transmission cycle of infection was broken by the development of the smallpox vaccine?

A. Vaccinated people are no longer susceptible hosts, so they are protected from getting the disease and passing on the pathogen, so the chain of transmission is broken.

6. Susceptible host – The person to whom the infection is passed. A susceptible host is any person at risk of infection. Any weakening of the human body's natural defence system can affect susceptibility (vulnerability) to infection. Examples of individuals that are particularly more susceptible to infection include:

- infants or older adults
- individuals receiving treatment which suppresses the immune system, such as chemotherapy for cancer, steroid medications for some long-term conditions, and medication prescribed following a successful organ transplant.
- individuals living with immune deficiency conditions such as diabetes, HIV or leukaemia.

The transmission of infection will occur when the infectious agent (a microorganism) leaves the reservoir or original host through a portal of exit, is passed on (transmission) and enters a portal of entry to infect a new susceptible host.

To cause an infection to be transmitted, each link in the transmission cycle must be present. Removing one link in the chain will stop the cycle of infection.

Common infections, resulting conditions, signs and symptoms, and how they may be transmitted

There are four main categories of microorganisms that may cause infection in the human body: bacteria, viruses, fungi, and protozoa. The following are examples of common infections, the resulting conditions, and how they may be transmitted from individual to individual.

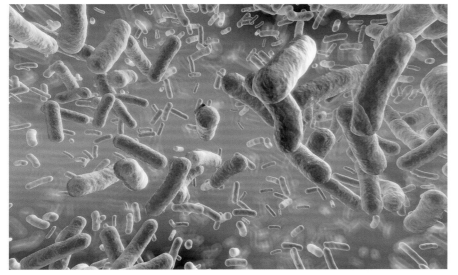

Bacterial Infections

Bacteria are the most common infection-causing pathogens. Hundreds of different bacteria can cause infection in the human body. These are transported through air, water, food, body fluids, body tissues and inanimate objects. Bacterial infections are usually treated with antibiotics, and the selection of the antibiotic will be based on the type of bacteria involved.

Condition		General signs and symptoms	Method of transmission
Bacterial meningitis *A bacterial infection*	Meningitis is the infection of the membranes that surround and protect the brain. One cause of meningitis is a bacterial infection that may be carried asymptomatically in the nose by infected individuals.	■ High fever ■ Severe headache ■ Stiff neck ■ Sensitivity to light ■ Skin rash that does not fade when a glass is rolled over it ■ Sickness	■ **Air-borne** transmission by inhaling the infection when the infected individual coughs or sneezes and another individual inhales the infected respiratory droplets. ■ **Direct** transmission by sharing respiratory and throat secretions (such as saliva) and close contact (for example, coughing or kissing).
Lyme disease *A bacterial infection*	Lyme disease causes inflammation that affects multiple human body systems.	■ Fatigue (extreme tiredness) ■ Joint pain and swelling of joints ■ High fever ■ Headaches ■ Flu-like symptoms	**Vector-borne** infection transmitted when ticks (spiderlike mites that live in wooded areas and long grass) transfer bacteria from wild animals and pass the bacteria to humans through their bites.
Pneumonia *A bacterial infection*	Pneumonia refers to the inflammation of the tissue of the lungs commonly caused by bacterial infection. It causes difficulty with breathing, chest pain and a cough.	■ Persistent cough ■ High fever ■ Sharp chest pain when breathing and coughing ■ Shortness of breath ■ Mucus (yellow, green or blood-stained) production	■ **Air-borne** transmission by inhaling the infection when the infected individual coughs or sneezes and another individual inhales the infected respiratory droplets. ■ **Vehicle-borne** transmission through the mouth or eyes when a person touches a surface that an infected individual has coughed or sneezed on.
Tuberculosis (TB) *A bacterial infection*	Tuberculosis (TB) is a bacterial infection affecting mainly the lungs. However, it can affect other areas of the human body, such as the musculoskeletal system, the nervous system, and the digestive system. According to Public Health Wales, there were 182 cases of TB in Wales during 2019–20 (this equates to 6.3 cases per 100,000 of the population).	■ Weight loss and lack of appetite ■ High fever ■ Fatigue (extreme tiredness) ■ Night sweats ■ Persistent cough ■ Blood-stained mucus	**Air-borne** transmission: individuals may be infected by inhaling the infection when an infected individual coughs or sneezes and another individual inhales the infected particles.

Fungal infections

Fungal infections can appear anywhere on the human body. Although most fungi are harmless to humans, some of them can cause diseases under specific conditions. Fungi thrive on the skin in warm, moist areas such as the groin, between the toes, and the mouth. Fungi also commonly affect nails, and more severe infections can affect the lungs. Fungal infections are usually treated with antifungal medications.

Condition		Signs and symptoms	Method of transmission
Fungal nail infection (Onychomycosis) *A fungal infection*	Onychomycosis is a fungal infection affecting toenails more than fingernails, although the infection may be transmitted to fingernails from contact with toenails.	Pain, thickening, flaking and discolouration of the nails.	■ **Direct** transmission through touching other infected nails. ■ **Vehicle-borne** transmission through contact with contaminated objects, such as shoes or socks, or walking barefoot on surfaces with fungal or yeast spores.
Ringworm (Tinea corporis) *A fungal infection*	Named ringworm due to the ring-shaped appearance of the rash; no worm is involved; a fungal infection causes it.	Red, itchy, and circular rash with a clear area of skin in the middle of the lesion.	■ **Direct** transmission involving contact from individual to individual (skin-to-skin) ■ **Vehicle-borne** transmission through touching an infected person's clothing, or even by touching a surface or object that has been in contact with an infected individual's skin.

Viral Infections

Viral infections are dependent on viruses reproducing by entering living cells of the human body. Viruses will infect a host cell by introducing their genetic material into the cells and taking over their normal functioning to produce other virus particles. Usually, no treatment is needed for viral infections, or in some cases, they are treated with antiviral medication.

Condition		Signs and symptoms	Method of transmission
Chickenpox *A viral infection*	The varicella-zoster virus causes chickenpox. It is a highly contagious infection; individuals may be infectious two days before signs appear and until the blisters have become crusted at around five days after they first appeared. It may take up to three weeks for signs and symptoms to appear following being infected.	■ High fever ■ A feeling of general illness ■ An itchy rash ■ Fluid-filled blisters	■ **Direct** transmission (by directly touching blisters, saliva, or mucus of an infected person) ■ **Air-borne** transmission (by inhaling – the infection can occur when an individual with chickenpox coughs or sneezes and another individual inhales the infected particles) ■ **Vehicle-borne** transmission (by touching contaminated items, such as the clothing of an infected individual).
Influenza (flu) *A viral infection*	A common acute respiratory infection affecting the nose, throat and lungs. In most cases, influenza will cause mild symptoms and clear within a few days. However, it can cause severe symptoms, and potentially death, in individuals living with compromised immune systems.	■ High fever ■ Headache ■ Cough ■ Sore throat ■ Stuffy nose ■ General fatigue	■ **Air-borne** transmission; inhaling the infection can occur when an individual with influenza coughs or sneezes and another individual inhales the infected particles. ■ **Direct** transmission by directly touching saliva or mucus of an infected individual

Protozoal infections

Protozoal infections are transmitted through ingestion of cysts (the dormant life stage of the protozoa) found in uncooked meat or cat faeces, sexual transmission, or through insects. Protozoa are found everywhere, often living in the soil or water. Treatment options depend on which of the protozoa is causing the infection.

Condition		Signs and symptoms	Method of transmission
Toxoplasmosis *A protozoal infection* 	Toxoplasmosis is an infection most often transmitted in the UK from the parasitic-infected faeces of cats. It can be caused by poor hand hygiene when changing cat litter or from contaminated soil when gardening.	▪ Usually asymptomatic ▪ General flu-like symptoms	**Vehicle-borne** transmission; ingestion of raw or inadequately cooked infected meat; ingestion of cysts that cats pass in their faeces, through exposure to cat litter or soil (e.g. from gardening) or unwashed fruits or vegetables.
Malaria *A protozoal infection* 	Malaria is a tropical disease. Most cases of malaria and deaths from malaria occur in sub-Saharan Africa, South-East Asia, the Eastern Mediterranean, Western Pacific, and the Americas. Some individuals are more susceptible to developing malaria symptoms and severe disease than others; these include babies, infants, children under five years of age, and individuals living with a compromised immune system.	▪ General flu-like symptoms ▪ High fever ▪ Headache ▪ Jaundice ▪ Convulsions	**Vector-borne** transmission: insects (mosquitoes) pick up the parasite found in the red blood cells of an infected person. When a mosquito lands on an infected individual, the mosquito takes a small amount of blood, which contains microscopic malaria parasites; these parasites mix with the mosquito's saliva and are injected into the next individual being bitten.

Parasitic infections

Parasitic infections can be transmitted in several ways; for example, through contaminated water, food, waste, soil, blood, and sexual contact. Some parasites can be spread by insects that act as a vector or carrier of the disease. Parasites live on other living organisms or hosts.

Some parasites do not visibly affect their hosts; however, other parasites will grow, reproduce, or enter human body systems, causing infection. Some parasitic infections do not require treatment, and the infection may disappear on its own. Some medicines are designed to eliminate parasites or reduce the number of worms enough to clear up symptoms. Certain antibiotics and antifungal medications are effective against some parasitic infections. However, for some parasitic infections, no drug is effective.

Condition		Signs and symptoms	Method of transmission
Lice *A parasitic infection* 	Lice are prevalent in individuals who mix in close contact with other individuals, such as children in school.	■ Itchy scalp ■ Feeling that something is crawling in the hair	■ **Direct** transmission; transferred from person to person by direct contact of hair. ■ **Vehicle-borne** transmission by touching contaminated items, such as clothing, of an infected individual.
Tapeworm *A parasitic infection* 	Tapeworms are flat worms that infest the digestive system when eggs are ingested by consuming infected foods, such as raw or undercooked meat. Individuals can also become infected if they come into contact with animal faeces or contaminated water.	■ Eggs in stools ■ Abdominal discomfort ■ Disturbed sleep ■ Altered appetite ■ Weight loss	**Vehicle-borne** transmission by the faecal-oral route can be transmitted by food and water contaminated with the tapeworm eggs or larvae.
Scabies *A parasitic infection*	Scabies is an itchy skin condition caused by mites that burrow into the outer layers of the skin.	■ Itching ■ A rash	**Direct** transmission transferred from person-to-person by direct and prolonged contact (skin-to-skin).

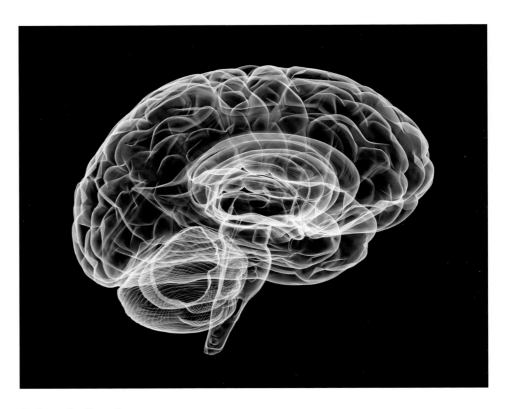

Prion infections

Microorganisms do not cause **prion infections**; a prion is a protein that can cause the usual proteins found in the brain to fold abnormally to cause neurodegenerative diseases (changes in memory, movement, and behaviour). Prion diseases can affect both humans and animals, hence transmission through infected meat products. Currently, there is no treatment for prion infections.

Condition		Signs and symptoms	Method of transmission
■ **Creutzfeldt-Jakob disease (CJD)** ■ **Sporadic Creutzfeldt-Jakob disease (CJD)** ■ **Variant Creutzfeldt-Jakob disease (vCJD)** *A prion infection*	CJD is a rare progressive and fatal condition affecting the brain and wider nervous system. The majority of individuals living with CJD will die within one year of symptoms starting.	■ Dementia-like symptoms ■ Loss of balance and coordination ■ Loss of eyesight ■ Loss of mobility	It is thought that an older form of prion disease found in sheep may have mutated and spread to cows fed meat from sheep containing traces of the mutated version of the prion. Individuals are then thought to have eaten contaminated beef products (there are now stringent farming regulations in the UK to avoid this transmission).
Iatrogenic Creutzfeldt-Jakob disease (iCJD)			**Vehicle-borne** transmission spread from an individual living with CJD through medical or surgical treatment.

Methods of transmission

Pathogen	Examples of a method of transmission
Bacteria	**Direct transmission:** sharing respiratory and throat secretions (saliva or spit) close contact (for example, coughing or kissing) or prolonged contact.
	Vehicle-borne transmission: faecal-oral route can be transmitted by contaminated food and water; through the mouth or eyes, a person touches a surface that an infected individual has coughed or sneezed on.
	Vector-borne transmission: Insects pick up bacteria from animals and pass the bacteria to humans through their bites.
	Air-borne transmission: Inhaling the infection can occur when an infected individual coughs or sneezes and another person inhales the infected particles.
Virus	**Direct transmission:** directly touching blisters, saliva, or mucus of an infected person; oral-to-oral or oral-to-genital contact (via contact with sores, saliva, and surfaces in or around the mouth and genitals); via the exchange of various body fluids from infected people, such as blood, breast milk, semen, and vaginal secretions; can also be transmitted from a mother to her child during pregnancy and delivery; via the exchange of blood from infected people; may also be transmitted when an infected individual is asymptomatic.
	Vehicle-borne transmission: through the mouth or eyes can happen when an individual with an infection is in contact with another individual. This can be by coughing or sneezing. It can also be transferred by touching contaminated items such as the clothes of an infected individual. The faecal-oral route can be transmitted by contaminated food and water.
	Air-borne transmission: inhaling the infection can occur when the infected individual coughs or sneezes and another person inhales the infected particles.
Fungi	**Direct transmission:** transferred from person-to-person by direct contact (skin-to-skin or nail-to-nail).
	Vehicle-borne transmission: contact with items contaminated with the fungi, such as shoes, socks, walking barefoot, or touching a changing-room bench or other object that has contacted an infected individual's skin.
	Air-borne transmission: inhaling fungal spores found in the environment.
Protozoan	**Vehicle-borne transmission:** ingestion of raw or inadequately cooked infected meat; ingestion of cysts that cats pass in their faeces through exposure to cat litter or soil (e.g. from gardening or unwashed fruits or vegetables).
	Vector-borne transmission: insects (such as mosquitoes) pick up the parasite found in the red blood cells of an infected person. When a mosquito bites an individual with malaria, it takes a small amount of blood containing parasites; these parasites mix with the mosquito's saliva, which is injected into the individual being bitten.
Parasites	**Direct transmission:** transferred from person-to-person by direct contact of hair; transferred from person-to-person by direct and prolonged contact (skin-to-skin).
	Vehicle-borne transmission: by touching contaminated items, such as clothing, of an infected individual; spread by the faecal-oral route and transmitted by food and water contaminated with the tapeworm eggs or larvae.
Prion	**Vehicle-borne transmission**: is spread from an infected individual through contact with infected tissue or inadequately sterilised medical or surgical treatment.

Activity

1. Some more examples of bacterial infections are:
   - ■ MRSA (Methicillin-resistant Staphylococcus Aureus)
   - ■ Clostridioides difficile (C. difficile)

   Independently research the above conditions to produce a mind-map or table for the signs and symptoms associated with each condition, and how each of the above conditions may be transmitted.

2. Some more examples of fungal infections are:
   - ■ Tinea pedis (athlete's foot)
   - ■ Candida albicans (oral thrush)

   Independently research the above conditions to produce a mind-map or table for the signs and symptoms associated with each condition, and how each of the above conditions may be transmitted.

3. Some more examples of viral infections are:
   - ■ Rhinovirus (common cold)
   - ■ Norovirus
   - ■ Measles
   - ■ Human Immunodeficiency Virus (HIV)
   - ■ Hepatitis A, Hepatitis B and Hepatitis C
   - ■ Herpes

   Independently research the above conditions to produce a mind-map or table for the signs and symptoms associated with each condition, and how each of the above conditions may be transmitted.

4. Another example of a protozoal infection is:
   - ■ Cryptosporidiosis

   Independently research the above condition to produce a mind-map or table for the signs and symptoms associated with the condition, and how it may be transmitted.

Task:

Produce a revision resource to outline the transmission cycle for one bacterial infection, one fungal infection, one viral infection, one protozoal infection, one parasitic infection, and one prion infection.

4.2: The causes and effects of a range of physiological conditions

You should know and understand the:

- causes of a range of physiological conditions
- effects that physiological conditions may have on individuals
- impact on the activities of daily living

Key term

A **physiological condition** is when the organs in the body malfunction and cause symptoms that may lead to illness.

Causes of physiological conditions

The ageing process

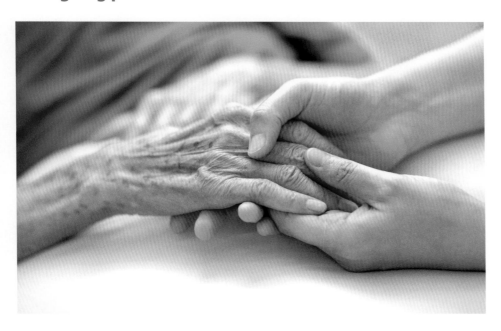

Data published by the Welsh Government in October 2018 showed that approximately 25% of the population of Wales was aged over 60 years, and over a third of those individuals were at least 75 years of age. Due to improvements in living standards in many parts of the world, it is expected that the proportion of the world's population over 60 years old will double by 2050 (WHO, 2018). With individuals living longer, care and support needs will change due to physiological conditions caused by the ageing process.

Some physiological conditions caused by the ageing process are dementia, osteoarthritis, and osteoporosis; although ageing is a risk factor for these conditions, they are not inevitable consequences of ageing.

Dementia	■ mainly affects older individuals diagnosed with symptoms that affect memory, thinking and behaviour, making daily living difficult ■ the effects may include: increased anxiety, depression, wandering, aggression and hallucination. Bladder incontinence is common in the later stages, and some individuals experience bowel incontinence, appetite and weight loss problems ■ it is estimated that around 525,000 individuals are living with dementia in the UK (*Dementia Statistics Hub*) ■ the risk of developing dementia rises with age
Osteoarthritis (OA)	■ a chronic degenerative joint condition ■ one of the most common causes of disability in older adults ■ frequently referred to as 'wear-and-tear' arthritis, due to adverse changes to the articular cartilage that protects the joints (the cartilage will gradually wear down, leaving the bones of a joint to rub against each other, causing damage, pain, swelling and stiffness) ■ research has shown that several factors cause OA to develop, and the exact cause is still unknown; joint injury, age, other conditions affecting the joints, obesity and genetics are thought to play a part
Osteoporosis	■ bone mass varies with age and, as the body ages, the density of bone deteriorates, resulting in osteoporosis (porous bone) ■ individuals living with osteoporosis are at a higher risk of bone fractures ■ individuals frequently live asymptomatically until a bone is fractured. When X-rays are taken, osteoporosis is confirmed

Autoimmune conditions

Autoimmune conditions occur when the mechanism that enables the immune system to recognise the difference between the body's cells and external cells breaks down; this causes the body to mistakenly attack its own cells. More than 80 different autoimmune conditions affect various body systems.

Common autoimmune conditions are multiple sclerosis (MS), insulin-dependent diabetes mellitus (IDDM), myasthenia gravis and rheumatoid arthritis.

Multiple sclerosis (MS)	■ a condition that affects the protective insulating tissue (myelin sheath) surrounding the nerves of the brain, the spinal cord, and the nerves around the body ■ causes challenges to body coordination, vision, balance, and sensation ■ severely limits nerve function
Type I diabetes mellitus	■ also referred to as insulin-dependent diabetes mellitus ■ caused when the immune system produces antibodies that destroy the pancreas cells involved in insulin production ■ results in the failure of the pancreas to produce insulin, which leads to the inability to control blood glucose
Myasthenia gravis	■ affects one in 30,000 individuals (mainly female) ■ it is a progressive condition; the skeletal muscles become gradually more unresponsive, resulting in breathing difficulties ■ antibodies produced by the immune system attack connections between the nerves and the skeletal muscles ■ results in the failure of the muscles to contract to allow movement
Rheumatoid arthritis (RA)	■ a progressive condition that causes inflammation and pain in the joints and other areas of the body, such as the eyes, cardiovascular system and respiratory system ■ the body's immune system does not recognise the lining of the joints, and mistakes these for external cells, resulting in the release of inflammatory chemicals

Nutritional deficiency

Nutritional deficiency refers to an insufficient quantity of vital nutrients (such as vitamins and minerals) in the diet, resulting in disease or malnutrition. Some people in Wales cannot afford healthy foods, instead relying on cheaper and more unhealthy options. Malnutrition is therefore common, not necessarily due to lack of food, but from eating less nutritious foods.

Two of the **most common nutritional deficiencies** seen in Wales are anaemia and rickets.

Anaemia	■ a condition affecting the blood
	■ a healthy number of circulating red blood cells (erythrocytes) containing a protein called haemoglobin are required to distribute oxygen around the body; if the haemoglobin level in the blood is low, or there are not enough erythrocytes, or the erythrocytes available are damaged, individuals will have insufficient oxygen circulating in the blood
	■ results in individuals feeling tired, cold, confused, unable to concentrate, having brittle nails, and, in severe cases, could result in changes to the heart, such as an irregular heartbeat (arrhythmia)
	■ several types of anaemia are linked to nutritional deficiencies, the most common being:
	■ **iron-deficiency anaemia**, which is caused by low levels of iron circulating in the blood, due to not enough iron being absorbed from the diet
	■ **folate-deficiency anaemia**, also referred to as megaloblastic anaemia, results from a lack of folic acid circulating in the blood, causing erythrocytes to be larger than usual
Rickets and osteomalacia	■ caused by a deficiency of vitamin D and/or calcium deficiency, resulting in the softening or weakening of bones in children
	■ common signs of rickets in children are muscle weakness, bowing of the legs, delayed growth and motor function, and pain in the legs, spine and pelvis
	■ in adults, a similar condition may be seen called osteomalacia, which is also due to a vitamin D deficiency; osteomalacia causes the same signs as rickets

Lifestyle choices

According to the World Health Organisation, lifestyle choices account for up to 60% of preventable diseases, significantly impacting physical and mental well-being. Some lifestyle choices that could lead to a greater risk of causing disease are unhealthy diets, a high BMI (body mass index), lack of exercise, tobacco smoking, drinking alcohol, substance misuse and stress.

Two of the **most common conditions caused by poor lifestyle choices** in Wales are alcohol-related liver disease and type 2 diabetes mellitus.

Alcohol-related liver disease	■ occurs due to long-term excessive alcohol consumption ■ the liver is the organ responsible for metabolising (breaking down) alcohol in the body; if the liver cannot keep up with metabolising large amounts of alcohol, and an individual continues to drink alcohol, the liver becomes damaged ■ initially, individuals who drink large quantities of alcohol will develop a fatty liver, where the liver will store glucose absorbed from the alcohol as fat, causing the liver to become enlarged ■ research suggests that if an individual stops drinking alcohol at this stage, then liver damage can be reversed ■ if alcohol continues to be consumed, the damage will progress, causing inflammation to the liver and permanent scarring, which cannot be reversed ■ this stage is referred to as liver cirrhosis
Type 2 Diabetes Mellitus	■ also referred to as non-insulin-dependent diabetes mellitus ■ occurs when the cells of the pancreas that produce insulin to regulate blood glucose levels do not produce enough insulin, or the insulin produced fails to reduce blood glucose levels ■ historically, type 2 diabetes has been diagnosed in individuals over 40 years of age due to obesity, lack of physical exercise and poor dietary choices ■ in recent years, type 2 diabetes has become widespread in children and adolescents due to no physical exercise, or very little physical exercise, and poor diets

Activity 2

Produce two posters (one on alcohol liver disease and one on type 2 diabetes mellitus) to advise individuals on:

■ the cause of these conditions
■ the risks associated with these conditions
■ what could be done to reduce the risk of developing these conditions

Inherited and genetic causes

Occasionally changes occur in the genes that individuals inherit from their parents, causing conditions present from birth that may affect daily living. If there is a family history of certain genetic conditions, parents planning a pregnancy may be offered genetic testing and genetic counselling.

Two of the **most common inherited conditions** seen in Wales are muscular dystrophy and cystic fibrosis.

Muscular dystrophy	■ there are several types of muscular dystrophy, which are all progressive conditions, causing the body's muscles to become weaker and eventually causing challenges with mobility ■ in some types of muscular dystrophy, individuals face challenges with breathing and heart function, which can be life-limiting ■ Duchenne's muscular dystrophy (DMD) is one of the most common forms of muscular dystrophy, which mainly affects males due to a mutation affecting the male genes. DMD can affect females, but it is very rare ■ DMD is usually diagnosed in early childhood, when the child starts to walk; it is the most severe form of muscular dystrophy, causing complex challenges, and individuals diagnosed only live to their late teens and early 20s, due to the effect on the muscles of the respiratory system
Cystic fibrosis (CF)	■ a condition affecting protein found in the cells of the mucous membranes of the respiratory and digestive systems causing excessive production of thick and sticky mucus ■ this thick and sticky mucus will cause inflammation that can lead to blockages and infections, making breathing and digesting food difficult ■ individuals living with CF must follow a physical therapy regime and take medication to reduce mucus and prevent infections ■ CF is a life-limiting condition; however, with advances in treatment options, including transplants, individuals living with CF can now live into their forties and beyond

Injury at birth

Occasionally during the birth process, especially during a difficult birth, injury can occur to the baby. Risk factors for injuries to babies at birth may be due to the baby's size, whether the baby is born prematurely, if labour is prolonged or if the mother is obese.

One such condition resulting from **injury at birth** is cerebral palsy.

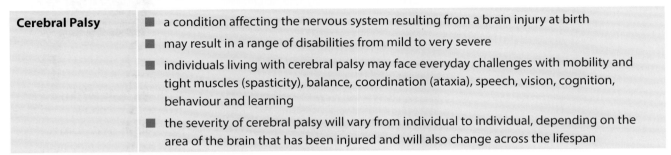

Cerebral Palsy	■ a condition affecting the nervous system resulting from a brain injury at birth
	■ may result in a range of disabilities from mild to very severe
	■ individuals living with cerebral palsy may face everyday challenges with mobility and tight muscles (spasticity), balance, coordination (ataxia), speech, vision, cognition, behaviour and learning
	■ the severity of cerebral palsy will vary from individual to individual, depending on the area of the brain that has been injured and will also change across the lifespan

The effects that physiological conditions may have on individuals and the impact on the activities of daily living

Mental and emotional health (of the individual, their family, friends, and wider circle)

■ Research has shown that there is a strong link between physical, mental and emotional health.

■ One study showed that up to one in three individuals living with long-term physiological conditions would also experience mental ill-health conditions, such as anxiety and depression. The impact of living with a physical and a mental health condition leads to poorer health outcomes and a reduced quality of life. Many individuals diagnosed with long-term physiological conditions affecting daily living activities will go through a grieving process before adjusting to their condition.

■ Very often, an individual living with a long-term physiological condition will experience a change in roles that may affect their sense of self and identity. Roles may alter relationships with family, friends, and their wider circle as their care and support needs change. Individuals may feel dependent on the individuals supporting them, which could either strengthen the relationship or strain these relationships. Family, friends, neighbours, support groups, religious and spiritual communities and healthcare providers may be necessary to assist at different times or for different reasons.

■ **Carers** may provide physical and practical assistance with activities of daily living, emotional support or medical assistance. Providing care and support for a family member or friend living with a long-term physiological condition affecting daily living activities can be highly demanding, both mentally and physically. Carers may also feel socially isolated, missing out on social interactions outside the home.

A **carer**, as defined by the Social Services and Well-being (Wales) Act 2014, is:

> any individual who cares, unpaid, for a friend or family member who, owing to illness, disability or an addiction cannot cope without their support.

Employment

Depending on the physiological condition and how the condition may impact the individual, employment challenges may be encountered. Very often, physiological conditions will impact employment due to early symptoms, such as fatigue and general malaise, before physical signs and symptoms become apparent. Employers have a legal duty of care to make reasonable adjustments to ensure that individuals living with physiological conditions can continue employment.

In the majority of cases, **making reasonable adjustments** may mean:

■ adapting workstations, such as providing height-adjustable desks or office chairs

■ changing the layout of a workspace to improve access

■ providing toilets or changing areas.

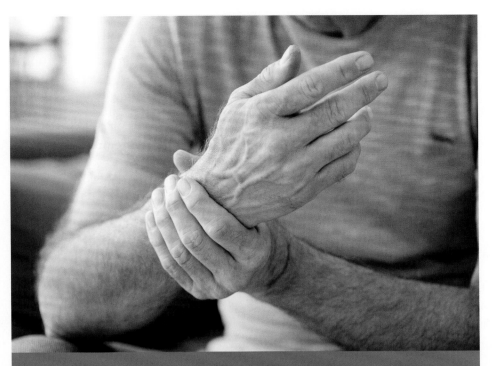

CASE STUDY

Scenario: Siôn is 46 years of age and has worked as an IT manager in a busy office for over 20 years. After several visits to his GP, complaining of fatigue and pain in his wrists and elbows, Siôn has recently been diagnosed with rheumatoid arthritis.

What reasonable adjustments could Siôn's employer make to ensure that his work does not impact on his condition?

Mobility

Many physiological conditions may affect mobility. This means that an individual may experience challenges with moving or walking. Examples of reduced mobility causes may be musculoskeletal pain, nerve pain, muscle weakness, paralysis, issues with balance, or obesity.

Challenges with mobility may result in an individual experiencing difficulty with daily living activities, such as requiring assistance with washing, dressing, preparing meals and attending employment and social activities.

Following a **care needs assessment**, an occupational therapist (OT) may assist individuals experiencing challenges with their mobility with home or work adaptations and equipment to encourage participation. Mobility aids, such as crutches, specialist wheelchairs or mobility scooters may be recommended to enable individuals to participate in daily living activities.

Activity

Walk around your home or college/school, making a list of potential concerns that an individual experiencing mobility challenges may face. What could be done to ensure mobility is maintained in these environments?

Nutritional intake and hydration

Adequate nutrition and hydration have a significant impact on general health.

Several physiological conditions may impact nutritional uptake; below are some examples:

Individuals living with dementia	May forget to eat or may require prompting to eat
Individuals living with conditions that impact swallowing (e.g. MS, myasthenia gravis, muscular dystrophy, stroke, or motor neurone disease)	May face challenges with swallowing food, which could lead to insufficient uptake of nutrients
	May feel embarrassed about eating slowly or making a mess
Individuals living with visual impairments	May be unable to prepare food

Certain medications prescribed for physiological conditions may also cause a reduction in appetite or may cause nausea.

Several physiological conditions may impact hydration; below are some examples:

Individuals living with dementia	May forget to drink or may require prompting to drink
Individuals living with conditions that may impact the musculoskeletal system (e.g. osteoarthritis)	May experience difficulties with lifting cups/glasses
Individuals living with conditions that impact bladder control	May worry about incontinence; therefore may drink less
	May worry about not being able to get the toilet in time, and may therefore drink less

Certain medications prescribed for physiological conditions may cause frequent urination; this can lead to dehydration if hydration is not maintained.

A chart similar to the one in the image below may be used in community healthcare settings to monitor nutrition and hydration.

All Wales Food and Fluid Record Chart for Community Settings

Please record all Food, Nutritional Supplements, Drinks and Nourishing drinks consumed. If NONE consumed please specify the reason on the chart.

Remember to:
- Record all food and drink consumed throughout the day
- Describe the type of food e.g. beef, bread, creamed potato
- Specify the quantity and meal size actually eaten e.g. ½ a small bowl of soup
- Specify the quantity of fluid consumed

Name:	Location:	Date:	Body wt kgs:
Date of birth:	Food Chart requested by:		Date recorded:

Meal/Snack	Foods / nutritional supplements / drinks / nourishing drinks / special diets eg pureed	Amount Taken				
		Portion served (SML)	Amount eaten (None, ¼, ½, ¾, All)	Fluid consumed (mls)	Fluid Output	Action and Signature
Breakfast Cereal Milk/Sugar Cooked items Bread/toast Spread Drinks						
Mid Morning Snacks Drinks						
Lunch Soup Main item Potato/Rice Vegetables Pudding Drinks						
Mid Afternoon Snacks Drinks						
Dinner Soup Main item Potato/Rice Vegetables Pudding Drinks						
Supper Snacks Drinks						
Night Time Snacks Drinks						
Total fluids consumed in 24 hours/Total fluid output in 24 hours						
Any other nutrition						

F9151011   WG 10-12532

Personal hygiene

Personal hygiene refers to maintaining the cleanliness of the human body. Daily living activities that involve personal hygiene include:

- washing (showering or bathing)
- oral care
- toileting
- hair care
- dressing

Some physiological conditions may result in individuals facing challenges with maintaining their personal hygiene:

- due to physical impairments or reduced levels of energy as a direct result of the condition
- due to mental ill-health or reduced cognitive function due to the impact of the condition on daily living.

Individuals may require assistance to maintain personal hygiene whilst maintaining their dignity and considering their cultural practices and beliefs around personal hygiene, which may result in the individual feeling dependent on others.

The impact on the individual of not being able to maintain personal hygiene will vary from individual to individual. Self-esteem, confidence, and general well-being may be impacted. Socially, individuals may be avoided if they have poor personal hygiene, resulting in them withdrawing from social activities, which can in turn lead to loneliness and isolation.

Psychological impact

Being diagnosed with a physiological condition may have a significant psychological impact on individuals. On diagnosis, individuals may experience:

- changes to their self-esteem
- concerns about the condition and its long-term effects
- feelings of anger, sadness or grief
- fear of treatment or medical procedures that they may have to go through
- fear or embarrassment of depending on others
- concerns regarding possible physical changes to appearance or body image

Activity

Choose one physiological condition that affects physical health. Produce a mind-map of the psychological effect on an individual diagnosed with your chosen condition.

Social interaction

Individuals diagnosed with certain physiological conditions may experience social difficulties that result in their withdrawal from social activities. Individuals may feel embarrassed at their diagnosis and having to explain their diagnosis. Certain physiological conditions that affect speech may result in individuals feeling that they cannot communicate verbally without assistance, and therefore may not feel comfortable in social situations.

Reading and further research

Age UK – Conditions and illnesses **https://www.ageuk.org.uk/information-advice/health-wellbeing/conditions-illnesses/**

Alzheimer's Research UK – Dementia Statistics Hub (**https://www.dementiastatistics.org/**

Arthritis Foundation **https://www.arthritis.org/**

Bobath Centre (Cerebral Palsy) **https://www.bobath.org.uk/**

Diabetes UK **https://www.diabetes.org.uk/**

MS Society **https://www.mssociety.org.uk/**

Muscular Dystrophy UK **https://www.musculardystrophyuk.org/**

National Assembly for Wales Finance Committee (October 2018) The cost of caring for an ageing population **https://senedd.wales/laid%20documents/cr-ld11773/cr-ld11773-e.pdf**

National Rheumatoid Arthritis Society **https://nras.org.uk/**

NHS Wales – All Wales Food and Fluid Record Chart for Community Settings **https://gov.wales/sites/default/files/publications/2019-06/all-wales-food-and-fluid-record-chart-for-community-settings.pdf**

Royal Osteoporosis Society **https://theros.org.uk/**

SCOPE **https://www.scope.org.uk/**

World Health Organisation (5 February 2018) Ageing and Health **https://www.who.int/news-room/fact-sheets/detail/ageing-and-health**

World Health Organisation (2 September 2021) Dementia **https://www.who.int/news-room/fact-sheets/detail/dementia#:~:text=Dementia%20is%20a%20syndrome%20in,million%20new%20cases%20every%20year**

4.3: How the human body is affected by common conditions

You should know and understand the:

- common conditions that occur in Wales
- impact common conditions have on the human body:
  - signs and symptoms
  - short-term and/or long-term effects
  - minor and/or major impact on daily living
  - care and support needs.

Certain conditions affecting the human body are commonly seen in Wales. Public Health Wales and the Welsh Government monitor these conditions and the impact they have on the human body to ensure that health and social care services are targeted towards the conditions prevalent in Wales.

Common conditions affecting the cardiovascular system

The cardiovascular system comprises the blood, the blood vessels around the body and the heart. Examples of some conditions that impact the cardiovascular system are coronary heart disease, angina, arrhythmia, and cerebrovascular accident (stroke).

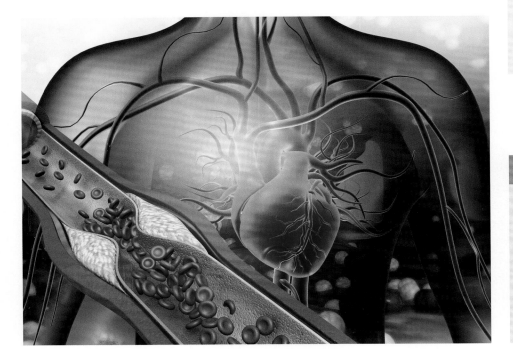

Key terms

Acute conditions – conditions that display severe and sudden symptoms; usually cured after a short time. However, acute conditions may lead to chronic conditions if left untreated.

Chronic conditions – conditions that develop and worsen over time.

Signs – observable characteristics that may be seen through observation, e.g. redness, swelling, temperature.

Symptoms – what the individual will feel and complain of, e.g. headaches, dizziness, nausea, cough, pain, and disorientation.

Activity 1

Research up-to-date statistics on the above conditions, i.e. how many people are affected in Wales, risk factors and treatment. Produce a mind-map showing your findings.

Condition		Signs/symptoms
Coronary heart disease *(physiological condition)*	Coronary heart disease is a condition where the arteries of the heart become blocked with fatty plaques (*atherosclerosis*), resulting in reduced blood flow to the cardiac (heart) muscle.	Coronary heart disease may vary depending on the individual – some individuals may experience severe symptoms; others may experience very little. Sign and symptoms generally include: ■ angina (see below) ■ dizziness ■ feeling faint ■ nausea or a feeling of indigestion ■ shortness of breath ■ abdominal pain ■ neck pain
Angina *(physiological condition)*	Angina refers to uncomfortable pain and pressure in the centre of the chest. This is caused by the narrowing of the arteries supplying the cardiac muscle with oxygen-rich blood.	Signs and symptoms of angina may vary depending on the individual; however, they generally include: ■ severe chest pain ■ heaviness and tightness in the chest ■ pain may extend to the neck, jaw, arms and back ■ symptoms may stop within minutes of resting
Arrhythmia *(physiological condition)*	An arrhythmia means an abnormality in how the heart maintains its rhythm (or beat). This may result in the heart beating too slowly (*bradycardia*) or too fast (*tachycardia*).	Signs and symptoms of an arrhythmia may vary depending on the individual; however, they generally include: ■ dizziness ■ feeling faint ■ palpitations (feeling of pounding or fluttering in the chest) ■ shortness of breath
Cerebrovascular accident *(physiological condition)*	A cerebrovascular accident (CVA, also known as stroke) occurs when part of the brain is deprived of blood rich in oxygen. There are two types of CVA: ■ **Ischaemic CVA** – the common type of CVA occurs when a blood clot blocks a blood vessel taking oxygen-rich blood to the brain, resulting in the brain being deprived of oxygen. ■ **Haemorrhagic CVA** – occurs when one of the blood vessels taking oxygen-rich blood to the brain is ruptured (has burst), resulting in the brain being deprived of oxygen.	Signs and symptoms of a CVA may vary depending on the individual and which area of the brain is deprived of oxygen. General signs and symptoms include: ■ sudden headache ■ loss of balance and coordination ■ numbness or paralysis in the face and arms or legs on one side of the body ■ difficulty verbalising

Common conditions affecting the respiratory system

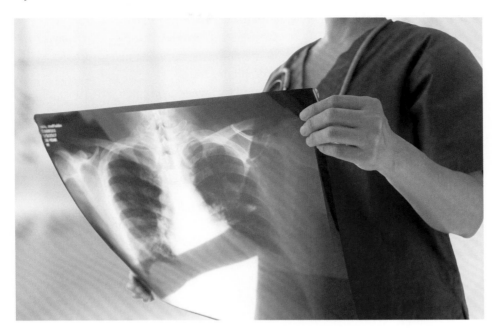

The respiratory system comprises the structures that aid breathing, the supply of oxygen to the body, and carbon dioxide from the body.

Examples of some conditions that impact the respiratory system are asthma, chronic obstructive pulmonary disease (COPD) and tuberculosis.

Condition		Signs/symptoms
Asthma (*physiological condition*)	Asthma refers to a condition caused by the narrowing and swelling of the airways, resulting in coughing, wheezing when breathing, and difficulty in breathing.	Signs and symptoms of asthma may vary depending on the individual; however, general signs and symptoms include: ■ shortness of breath ■ a wheezing sound when exhaling ■ a tight chest or chest pain
Chronic obstructive pulmonary disease (COPD) (*physiological condition*)	Chronic obstructive pulmonary disease (COPD) is a chronic lung condition causing the airways to become obstructed, resulting in difficulty breathing. COPD is a term used for many chronic respiratory conditions such as emphysema (damage to the lungs' alveoli) and bronchitis (inflammation of the airways).	Signs and symptoms of COPD may vary depending on the individual; however, general signs and symptoms include: ■ shortness of breath ■ a phlegm-producing cough ■ a wheezing sound on inhaling and exhaling ■ recurring chest infections

| Whooping cough *(infectious condition)* | Whooping cough (also known as pertussis) is caused by a bacterium that infects the respiratory system. It mainly affects babies from birth-6 months old, although teenagers and adults may also be affected. | First signs and symptoms of whooping cough may vary depending on the individual; however, general signs and symptoms include:
■ general malaise
■ flu-like symptoms – runny nose, fever
■ mild dry cough
Around two weeks after infection, the following symptoms may occur:
■ long coughing bouts lasting more than a minute
■ coughing with a "whooping" sound
■ appears to be gasping for air |
| Influenza *(infectious condition)* | Influenza (or flu) is a condition affecting the respiratory system caused by a virus that infects the respiratory tract. | Signs and symptoms of influenza may vary depending on the individual; however, general signs and symptoms include:
■ a fever
■ chills (feeling cold despite fever)
■ headache
■ runny nose
■ sore throat
■ cough
■ fatigue |

Activity 2

Research up-to-date statistics on the above conditions, i.e. how many people are affected in Wales, risk factors and treatment. Produce a mind-map showing your findings.

Common conditions affecting the nervous system

The nervous system is responsible for maintaining control in the human body, protection, and memory and learning.

A condition that impacts the nervous system is meningitis.

Condition		Signs/symptoms
Meningitis *(infectious condition)*	Meningitis is an infection of the membranes surrounding and protecting the brain; it may be bacterial or viral meningitis. **Viral meningitis:** is the most common, caused by a virus affecting the membranes of the brain; symptoms are usually mild and clear within 14 days. **Bacterial meningitis:** is not as common, and occurs when bacteria infect the membranes of the brain; however, it is more severe, with numerous potential complications.	Signs and symptoms of meningitis may vary depending on the individual; however, general signs and symptoms include: ■ stiff neck ■ headaches ■ fever ■ cold hands and feet ■ vomiting ■ photophobia (dislike of bright lights) ■ confusion ■ non-blanching rash

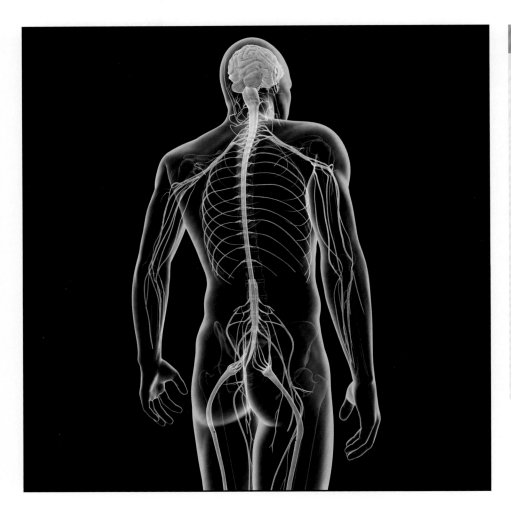

Activity 3

Some more examples of conditions affecting the nervous system are:
■ Spinal injury
■ Motor neurone disease (MND)
■ Cerebral palsy
■ Parkinson's disease
■ Peripheral neuropathy
■ Multiple sclerosis (MS)

Independently research the above conditions to produce a mind-map or table on the signs and symptoms associated with each condition and treatment options for each condition.

Common conditions affecting the endocrine system

Some more examples of conditions affecting the endocrine system are:
- Diabetes insipidus
- Hypothyroidism
- Hyperthyroidism

Independently research the above conditions to produce a mind-map, or table on the signs and symptoms associated with each condition and treatment options for each condition.

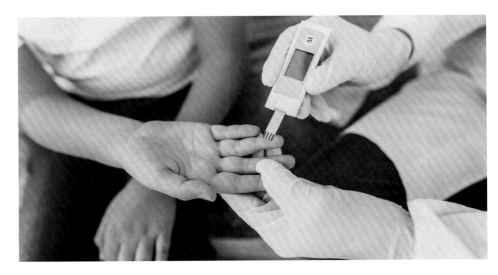

Through a complex network of glands and organs, the endocrine system is responsible for regulating hormone levels in the body. Growth, development, metabolism, and reproduction rely on the endocrine system.

A condition that affects the endocrine system is diabetes (type 1 and type 2).

Condition		Signs/symptoms
Diabetes mellitus (*physiological condition*)	Type I diabetes mellitus (also called insulin-dependent diabetes mellitus) is caused when the immune system produces antibodies that destroy the pancreas cells involved in insulin production. This results in the failure of the pancreas to produce insulin, which leads to the inability to control blood glucose. Type I diabetes mellitus is most commonly diagnosed in childhood and adolescence, although some adults may be diagnosed. Type 2 diabetes mellitus (also referred to as non-insulin-dependent diabetes mellitus) occurs when the cells of the pancreas that produce insulin to regulate blood glucose levels do not produce enough insulin, or the insulin produced fails to reduce blood glucose levels. Historically, type 2 diabetes has been diagnosed in individuals over 40 years old due to obesity, lack of physical exercise and poor dietary choices. In recent years, type 2 diabetes has become widespread in children and adolescents, due to no physical exercise, or very little physical exercise, and poor dietary choices at an earlier age.	General signs and symptoms of type I and type II diabetes mellitus include: - feeling of thirst - frequent urination, especially at night - general malaise - unintended loss of weight - blurred vision - cuts and grazes that take a long time to heal - a fruit-like odour to the breath

Common conditions affecting the digestive system

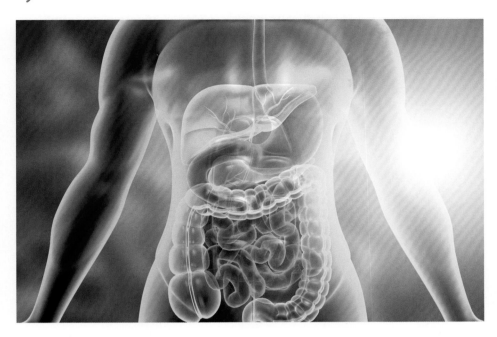

The digestive system breaks down food and enables nutrients to be absorbed into the bloodstream to be used around the body.

A condition that impacts the endocrine system is norovirus.

Activity 5

Some more examples of conditions affecting the digestive system are:
- Crohn's disease
- Coeliac disease
- Irritable bowel syndrome (IBS)
- Ulcerative colitis

Independently research the above conditions to produce a mind-map or table on the signs and symptoms associated with each condition and treatment options for each condition.

Condition		Signs/symptoms
Norovirus *(infectious condition)*	Norovirus (also referred to as the 'winter vomiting bug') is caused by a virus that leads to severe vomiting and diarrhoea lasting up to two days.	General signs and symptoms of norovirus include: - nausea - vomiting - diarrhoea - fever - headache - general malaise (tired, feeling ill)

Common conditions affecting several body systems

Examples of **infectious conditions** include influenza, measles, meningitis, MRSA, mumps, norovirus, tuberculosis (TB) and whooping cough.

Condition		Signs/symptoms
Tuberculosis *(infectious condition)*	Tuberculosis (TB) is caused by inhaling droplets from the coughs of an individual infected by a bacterium known as *Mycobacterium tuberculosis*. TB mainly affects the lungs; however, it can affect all parts of the body, including the nervous system, the renal system, and the musculoskeletal system.	Signs and symptoms of TB may vary depending on the individual and which part of the body is affected; however, general signs and symptoms include: ■ a persistent blood-stained phlegm-producing cough ■ enlarged lymph glands ■ general malaise ■ loss of appetite and weight ■ fever and night-sweats ■ fatigue
Sepsis *(infectious condition)*	Sepsis can be a life-threatening condition caused by the body's immune system over-reacting to an infection. Sepsis is often called blood poisoning or septicaemia. Sepsis does not just affect the blood, however, and may affect the whole body, including the organs.	Signs and symptoms of sepsis may vary depending on the individual and which part of the body is affected; however general signs and symptoms include: ■ increased heart rate ■ low blood pressure (hypotension) ■ fever and/or shivering ■ confusion ■ breathlessness ■ pain and/or discomfort ■ clammy skin
MRSA *(infectious condition)*	MRSA (methicillin-resistant *staphylococcus aureus*) is a bacterium that may infect any part of the body; it is resistant to common antibiotics, and is not easily treatable. Around one in three people carry this bacterium on their skin or nose. This does not cause a problem in healthy individuals. In individuals who are immunocompromised or susceptible to infection (such as infants or older adults), it can cause severe infection.	Usual signs and symptoms of an MRSA infection of the skin include: ■ redness of an area of skin ■ inflammation ■ pain ■ fever ■ cuts/sores or wounds taking a long time to heal Usual signs and symptoms of an internal MRSA infection include: ■ fever and/or shivering ■ confusion ■ general malaise (tired, feeling ill) ■ breathlessness

→

Measles (*infectious condition*)	Measles is a highly infectious condition affecting the respiratory system, causing a body rash and general malaise. Despite being a respiratory condition, it may affect other body systems, such as the central nervous system, causing blindness, convulsions, and severe dehydration.	Usual signs and symptoms of measles include: ■ fever ■ runny nose ■ cough ■ photophobia (dislike of bright lights) ■ distinctive rash
Mumps (*infectious condition*)	Mumps is a viral infection that initially causes swelling of the salivary glands in the face and neck. Occasionally, mumps will cause severe complications (especially in adults) such as: ■ inflammation of the testes and ovaries ■ inflammation of the pancreas ■ inflammation of the brain and the membranes surrounding the brain (as in meningitis) ■ deafness	Signs and symptoms of mumps may vary depending on the individual, with some individuals not experiencing any symptoms; however, general signs and symptoms include: ■ fever ■ headache ■ neck pain ■ loss of appetite ■ general malaise (tired, feeling ill)

Activity 6

Some other examples of conditions that may affect several body systems are:
■ Shingles
■ Rheumatoid arthritis
■ Muscular dystrophy
■ Polycystic ovary syndrome (PCOS)
■ Autoimmune conditions

Independently research the above condition to produce a mind-map or table on the signs and symptoms associated with the condition and treatment options for the condition.

Allergies

Activity 7

Allergies are becoming more common. Research shows that allergies are more common in developed countries than in developing countries. Can you suggest why this may be the case?

The term allergies may be used for many conditions causing overstimulation of the immune system. Examples of allergies include skin reactions such as urticaria (hives), food allergies, hay fever, dust allergies and the inflammatory response responsible for asthma and eczema.

The result of an allergy will vary from person to person. The majority of individuals will experience very mild reactions that are treatable with over-the-counter medication such as antihistamines. Others may experience life-threatening anaphylaxis reactions requiring medications such as adrenaline, and will carry medication at all times in case of a reaction.

Examples of allergies, and the areas of the body impacted by allergies, are shown in the table below:

Allergy	Area impacted	Signs and symptoms
Hay fever	Sinuses and nasal cavity	Sneezing, itching inside the nose, runny nose, and red eyes
Urticaria (hives)	Skin	An itchy raised rash that usually disappears after a day or two
Food allergies	Digestive system	Usually short-lived diarrhoea
Asthma	Respiratory system	Shortness of breath, a tight chest and a wheezing sound when exhaling
Anaphylaxis	Systemic (i.e. whole body affected)	Urticaria (hives), difficulty with breathing, constricted airways, vomiting, low blood pressure, increased heart rate, abdominal pain, and vomiting

Cancer

The term cancer is used to describe a group of diseases defined by changes in the body's cells that may spread from their original area to other areas of the body. Cancer begins when the cells divide (via mitosis) uncontrollably, leading to a lump or tumour being formed. Several factors may make some individuals more susceptible to developing cancer than others, including lifestyle, environment and genetic factors.

There are over 200 different types of cancers affecting different parts of the body. The most common cancers diagnosed in Wales, which account for more than half of cancers, are:

- colon/bowel cancer
- prostate cancer
- breast cancer
- lung cancer

Other areas of the human body commonly affected by cancer include the kidney, pancreas, bladder, leukaemia, ovary, uterus, brain, and oesophagus.

Activity 8

It is difficult to predict why one individual will develop cancer, and another will not. However, research suggests that some risk factors may increase an individual's chance of developing cancer.

Research the risk factors associated with the cancers listed above and produce a revision resource (such as a poster or notes) to discuss in class.

Short-term effects of living with common conditions

Some possible short-term effects of living with a condition could include:

- general malaise (tired, feeling ill)

- fatigue

- coping with pain

- frustration, anger, and anxiety, knowing that a condition is going to progress

- impact of adjusting to medication
  - medication regime
  - side-effects

- lifestyle changes such as changes to diet, exercise, stop smoking, reducing alcohol intake and reducing stress

- adjusting to frequent GP and/or hospital check-ups and monitoring appointments

Long-term effects of living with common conditions

Some possible long-term effects of living with a condition could include:

- cognitive changes to thinking, learning and planning

- emotional changes leading to depression

- changes in the ability to communicate

- loss of coordination and balance, causing mobility challenges and a higher risk of falls

- risk of comorbidity (if diagnosed with one condition, there is an increased likelihood of being diagnosed with others)

- risk of poly-pharmacy (being prescribed many different medications)

- reduced immunity as a result of either the condition or effects of medication, leading to an increased risk of infections, such as pneumonia or MRSA

- living with stigma associated with lifestyle causes of some conditions

Impact on daily living

Living with a condition will affect individuals differently, depending on individual circumstances and the condition diagnosed. Some conditions are progressive conditions, which means they will not impact daily life immediately. Instead, an individual's routine will need to change over time to allow for increasing difficulty with regular activities.

Some possible examples of the impact on daily living include:

- there is a time commitment/burden from good management of some conditions (e.g. lifestyle changes to diet, exercise, and taking medication exactly as described and managing side-effects) whilst doing everyday living activities

- social interactions may be difficult due to others' lack of knowledge of the condition

- employment opportunities may be restricted, particularly if a job requires shift work, which could interfere with medication or treatment regimes

- there may be implications for driving, depending on the type and severity of the condition

- extra planning may be required for travel and holidays, e.g. to ensure a sufficient supply of medication is available and that dietary needs can be catered for

- emotional impact

- psychological impact

- effects on family life, relationships, work and social activities

- reduced mobility and physical weakness may lead to difficulty in performing activities of daily living such as, for example, dressing, standing, walking, and personal hygiene

- risk of falls could be minimised with input from professionals such as an occupational therapist to provide home adaptations or a physiotherapist to provide a range of exercises.

Reading and further research

Allergy UK **https://www.allergyuk.org/**

British Heart Foundation **https://www.bhf.org.uk/**

British Lung Foundation **https://www.blf.org.uk/**

Cancer Research UK: cancer incidence statistics **https://www.cancerresearchuk.org/health-professional/cancer-statistics/incidence**

NHS: Health A–Z **https://www.nhs.uk/conditions/**

Public Health Wales: Welsh Cancer Intelligence and Surveillance Unit **https://phw.nhs.wales/services-and-teams/welsh-cancer-intelligence-and-surveillance-unit-wcisu/**

Royal College of Occupational Therapists **https://www.rcot.co.uk/about-occupational-therapy/what-is-occupational-therapy**

ACTIVITY ANSWERS
Activity 7

In developed countries, recent research has resulted in the adoption of a 'hygiene hypothesis'. This hypothesis states that less exposure to dirt and germs, in addition to a reduction in microbial exposure by children, has shown a reduced ability to withstand infection due to a 'westernised lifestyle'.

4.4: Care and support when living with physiological conditions and challenges

You should know and understand the:

- care and support needs of individuals living with physiological conditions
- differing models of health and well-being

Care and support needs

Assets and strengths

A **strengths-based approach to care and support** values the ability, the skills, the knowledge, the connections, and the potential of individuals requiring care, their friends, their family and wider circle when living with conditions affecting daily living activities. These factors are considered to be 'assets'.

By focusing on the assets and the strengths of an individual living with a condition that impacts on daily living, health and social care practitioners will not ignore the challenges individuals face; instead, they will look at the positives, to enable a strengths-based approach to the care provided.

Diagnosis and monitoring of the condition

Diagnosis of a condition may be made by:

- a doctor, either a general practitioner (GP) working in a local surgery or a specialist Consultant working in a hospital

- registered specialist nurses and midwives

- a range of allied health professionals trained to diagnose, such as podiatrists, orthoptists, and physiotherapists.

The term **diagnosing** describes the process of analysing signs and symptoms, whilst the term **diagnosis** describes a statement or conclusion to diagnosing a condition. Diagnosing may involve looking at the individual's medical history, a physical examination, scans and X-rays, blood and urine tests or a minor operation (such as taking a biopsy).

Following a diagnosis, monitoring a condition may involve regular follow-up appointments with a GP, hospital consultant or specialist nurse. Scans, blood and urine tests and physical examinations may be used to monitor a condition.

Assessment of care and support needs

A multi-disciplinary team (usually led by a registered practitioner, with input from occupational therapy and a healthcare team) will assess the care and support needs of the individual requiring care. The individual and their family/carer will also be involved, and have input into the assessment, to ensure that the care and support plan is person-centred. Therefore, the individual should be empowered by having a voice/choice/control over their care and support received, which increases the individual's independence and self-esteem needs.

Activity 1

Choose two conditions listed in Chapter 4.2 and Chapter 4.3 and explain how each condition is diagnosed and monitored to maintain well-being.

An assessment of needs aims to:

- ensure that the individual's well-being needs are met
- ensure the individual has voice, choice and control over care and support received
- assist the individual to be as independent as possible.

The assessment will include determining the goals and the desired outcomes of the individual receiving care and support, and how these will be achieved. The results of assessments will be different for each individual.

A carer's assessment may also be undertaken, if appropriate, to ensure that the rights of carers are upheld, and to identify support services that the carer may benefit from.

Interventions, care, support, and advice to improve well-being

Following an assessment of care and support needs, a personal care and support plan will be developed based on the individual's goals or desired outcomes.

Interventions may involve:

- assistance with mobility, speech and cognitive impairments related to a condition
- advice to improve health and well-being
- provision of aids and adaptations to the home to aid independence
- support with routine living tasks where mobility may be affected

■ support with mental health issues as a result of living with a condition, e.g. support groups, counselling

■ providing family, carers and the public with information and education on the condition, the impact for the individual living with the condition, and advice on how best to support them.

Respite care

Very often, providing care to a relative, a friend, or a neighbour takes a considerable amount of time. Respite care, therefore, aims to provide carers with a rest from their caring role. It offers carers the time to look after their own health and well-being. Respite care may improve the relationship between the carer and the individual receiving care and support, and gives the individual receiving care and support the opportunity to interact with others outside their usual circle.

Respite care may be provided in the individual's own home, in day centres, a hospice, or residential or nursing care homes.

Rehabilitation programmes

Rehabilitation programmes aim to enable individuals living with conditions to return to independence. When individuals live with a chronic or long-term condition, they may be required to adjust their lifestyles, especially if the condition causes complications that can lead to challenges.

Rehabilitation programmes usually involve a range of health professionals, such as an occupational therapist, a physiotherapist and a speech and language therapist.

Examples of rehabilitation programmes include:

- cardiac rehabilitation programmes aimed at individuals who have experienced a myocardial infarction (heart attack) or who have undergone heart bypass surgery

- neurological rehabilitation programmes aimed at individuals living with the effects of traumatic brain injuries

- mobility rehabilitation programmes aimed at individuals who have had a joint replacement.

Activity 2

Choose two conditions listed in Chapter 4.2 and Chapter 4.3 and prepare an information leaflet for each condition to show:
- how rehabilitation programmes may benefit individuals living with these conditions
- the range of health and social care professionals who may be involved in rehabilitation programmes.

Models of health and well-being

Learners should be able to apply the different models of health and well-being to a range of physiological conditions.

There are three models of health and well-being:

1. The social model of health and well-being

The social model of health and well-being focuses on how social, economic, and environmental factors influence health and well-being, and considers the environment (such as poor housing, pollution, poor diet and poverty) as the cause of illness. It also suggests that individuals are excluded by societal barriers, not by their health, impairment, or difference.

Positive aspects:	■ encourages social change by providing access to health and social care services ■ empowers individuals to make decisions about their own health
Negative aspects:	■ relies on individuals choosing to receive or understand health promotion information ■ relies on individuals' motivation to make changes to their behaviours

2. The medical model of health and well-being

The medical model of health and well-being assumes that illness or disease exists, and considers "health" as the absence of disease. It emphasises clinical diagnosis (laboratory tests) and medical intervention (e.g. medication) in treating a disease or its symptoms.

Positive aspects:	■ recognises that most illnesses may be treated with medical intervention ■ has led to advances in treatment options, such as cancer treatments
Negative aspects:	■ does not consider that there may be other factors causing illness ■ sees an individual living with a disability as a problem, and therefore they are limited by their condition ■ focuses on treatment, and not on health education and health promotion, to reduce risks of illness

Activity 3

Choose one condition listed in Chapter 4.2 and Chapter 4.3. Then, with reference to the social model, medical model and the biosychocial model assess the care and support that will support those individuals, their family, friends and others require to deal with the condition.

3. The biopsychosocial model of health and well-being

The biopsychosocial model of health and well-being incorporates interactions between biological, psychological and social factors to help determine why an individual might have a disorder.

Positive aspects:	■ views an individual as a complete person living with complex factors affecting health and well-being ■ integrates healthcare and social care services ■ care and support are tailored to the individual
Negative aspects:	■ assumes that all illnesses (especially mental ill-health) are biopsychosocial ■ considers the effects of society on the individual; however, it could be seen as impractical to consider all social factors when diagnosing or treating an individual.

> The medical support keeps me alive, but it is the psychological and social support that enables me to live.
>
> *The Patient Patient, 2013*

Reading and further research

Cardiac Rehabilitation, British Heart Foundation
**https://www.bhf.org.uk/informationsupport/support/practical-support/
cardiac-rehabilitation?gclid=CjwKCAjwk6-LBhBZEiwAOUUDp6xzU-PvY
JADp0ApgRqkqM9OgHrxlnZROzQpbxdWEQU1CuHkgY4kchoCdOwQA
vD_BwE&gclsrc=aw.ds**

Mobility rehabilitation
**https://www.physio.co.uk/treatments/neurological-rehabilitation/
mobility-rehabilitation.php**

Neurological rehabilitation
**https://www.royalfree.nhs.uk/services/neurosciences?q=%2Fservice
s%2Fservices-a-z%2Fneurosciences%2Fneurological-rehabilitation-
centre-nrc%2F#tab-overview**

4.5: Risk reduction strategies that can be implemented to support health and well-being

You should know and understand the:

- main current initiatives and health promotion strategies which can be implemented to support health and well-being.

Risk reduction strategies that individuals living with a diagnosed condition could apply to support their health and well-being could include:

- adhering to a prescribed medication regime
- adaptations to the home to reduce the risk of falls due to mobility challenges
- attending regular review appointments with the health and social care multi-disciplinary team, including for example, hospital consultants, specialist nurses, GP, community nurses, occupational therapists, physiotherapists, and registered practitioners
- engaging in more physical activity to maintain mobility
- reducing stress levels by looking after personal well-being.

Increasing public awareness of the conditions

Health promotional activities can raise awareness by, for example, organising local and national fundraising events, setting up specific support networks and by influencing politicians on national policies.

Increasing public awareness of services available

Third-sector organisations on a national and local level assist in increasing public awareness of the effects of conditions affecting the human body. These organisations also educate the public on health and social care services available to individuals living with conditions and their families, who may provide support and activities to promote their health and well-being.

Often, third-sector organisations will:

- offer information about the condition

- provide information and support for individuals living with a condition

- provide information on where individuals living with a condition may be able to access appropriate care and support services

- organise a support network for families, friends and the wider circle caring for individuals living with a condition

- offer information on treatment and therapies that may be useful when living with a condition

- provide up-to-date information and resources for health professionals providing care and support to individuals living with a condition

- organise local and national fundraising events to raise awareness of a condition, e.g.
  - organising challenges and events to raise sponsorship and provide fundraising resources and ideas
  - national fundraising by organising for example, running in a marathon, baking and selling cakes in a cake sale or wearing a specific costume or colour
  - local fundraising often organised by local support groups
  - corporate fundraising – large companies or organisations may make a charity their 'charity of the year'.

- raise awareness by influencing politicians on national policies that may affect care and support services for individuals living with a condition.

Knowledge of current initiatives and health promotion strategies

Initiatives and health promotion strategies are aimed at individuals living with conditions affecting the human body or aimed at reducing the risk of developing conditions. These strategies promote:

- improved nutrition and hydration

- the reduction of body weight in individuals with a high BMI

- adhering to prescribed medication regimes

- the importance of attending regular appointments

- engaging in more physical activity to maintain mobility

- reducing stress levels by looking after personal well-being

Activity 1

Examples of organisations that aim to raise awareness of services available are:
- Parkinson's UK Cymru
- Age Cymru
- National Rheumatoid Arthritis Society (NRAS)
- Target Ovarian Cancer
- The UK Sepsis Trust

Investigate the organisations listed above to enable you to prepare a mind map of the their services. Services that aims to raise the awareness of the public in the condition.

Choose a range of organisations that represent the conditions listed in Chapters 4.2 and 4.3. Undertake an investigation of how these specific organisations raise awareness within their specific organisation.

Activity 2

Can you think of some initiatives or health promotion strategies implemented to support health and well-being in Wales aimed at risk reduction?

Person-centred approach to care and support – positive risk-taking

Positive risk-taking involves weighing up the advantages and disadvantages of taking risks. The aim of positive risk-taking in a health and social care context and person-centred approach to care and support is to enable individuals receiving care and support to take risks to improve their quality of life and manage those risks.

Taking risks is a part of all our daily lives; by not taking risks, barriers would prevent us from achieving our goals. When health and social care professionals work with vulnerable individuals to promote their right to make choices, it may include taking risks. Positive risk-taking means that the individual will not be discouraged from taking a risk. It means that the health and social care professional will support the individual to understand what the risk is, and how it may be managed. By managing positive risk-taking, the individual's health and well-being will also be promoted.

By enabling the individual to make an informed choice about risk-taking and supporting positive risk-taking, health and social care professionals promote the individual's strengths. It will assist the individual to learn from the risk that they may take and understand the consequences of taking the risk.

Supporting individuals receiving care and support to take risks will result in enabling the individual:

- to develop resilience
- to gain independence, self-confidence, and self-esteem
- to recognise their right to make choices and decisions about their own life.

Risk assessment and assessing the impact of a risk is essential when supporting individuals to make choices. It involves an equilibrium between providing support to the individual to make their own choices whilst also supporting the right to make a choice. This will require the health and social care professional to practise within the legislation to ensure that individuals are kept safe [the Health and Safety at Work Act 1974] whilst maintaining their rights to make choices [The Social Services and Well-being (Wales) Act 2014, The Human Rights Act (1998) and the Mental Capacity Act (2005)].

Sexual health clinics: support, diagnose and offer treatment which reduces the stigma around STIs.

Substance misuse support: talking to someone is the first step in getting the help needed, and there is a 24/7 online and telephone contact service for alcohol and drug misuse support. Substance misuse can affect people regardless of their age, background, or ethnic origin, and can lead to significant problems affecting an individual's health, well-being, social circumstances, and the people around them.

Strengths-based and outcome-focused care

Outcome-focused care describes what an individual would like to achieve through realistic goals that the individual, their family, or carer can work towards to support health and well-being. Outcomes will vary from person to person, as they will be led by what matters to the individual.

An outcome-focused approach to care:

- enables a strengths-based approach to care, support and inclusion

- allows for the implementation of a person-centred care approach and related support

- focuses on what each individual can do to bring to the fore their own skills, strengths, and abilities. It also highlights of the importance of the community network

- it allows for each individual to be heard, listened to, and their wishes acted upon in providing care and support

- enables individuals to be equal partners in decisions made about their care and the support services they access

- empowers individuals and improves self-awareness, self-care, and allows them to have a greater understanding of advocacy services

- allows for health and social care services to be provided in a seamless way, meeting the needs of each individual, and delivered as close to home as possible

- draws attention to the fact that safeguarding is everyone's responsibility. Each individual professional and organisation is required to do everything they can to ensure that children and adults at risk are protected from abuse, improper treatment, neglect, or harm.

A strengths-based approach to care and support shows in a holistic way the individual's abilities, strengths, and their circumstances, rather than making the challenges that they may face the focus. It includes supporting individuals to overcome barriers to support health and well-being.

A critical point of a strengths-based and outcome-focused approach to care and support is that it is not about the result or the outcome/goal, but it is about how things are done. It is about how health and social care professionals use their skills when collaborating with individuals, their families, and the community that they live in to resolve a particular situation. The aim is to enable improved health and well-being outcomes for individuals.

Providing care and support services in a strengths-based and outcome-focused way does not mean providing individuals with fewer support

Activity 4

Choose two health conditions listed in Chapters 4.2 and 4.3. Describe the risk-reduction strategies that could be implemented to support the health and well-being of individuals living with these health conditions..

services. It means collaborating with individuals to identify the best way to use their strengths and the resources they currently have or may have access to. In the same way, it means that the correct assistance, advice, and support is available to individuals when they require it.

Reading and further research

Age Cymru **https://www.ageuk.org.uk/cymru/**

National Rheumatoid Arthritis Society (NRAS) **https://nras.org.uk/**

Parkinson's UK Cymru
https://www.parkinsons.org.uk/cy/about-us/parkinsons-uk-cymru

Target Ovarian Cancer **https://targetovariancancer.org.uk/?gclid= Cj0KCQjwnoqLBhD4ARIsAL5JedLTlaiajwPQW0r8ABwHk7nYs_ Hb0fgVvWSj8NLRIN9jkvw0fRFdGCgaApQXEALw_wcB**

The UK Sepsis Trust **https://sepsistrust.org/**

ACTIVITY ANSWER
Activity 2 Examples

Help Me Quit
Beat Flu
Designed to Smile
Keep Well, Keep Warm, Keep Safe
Talk to me 2

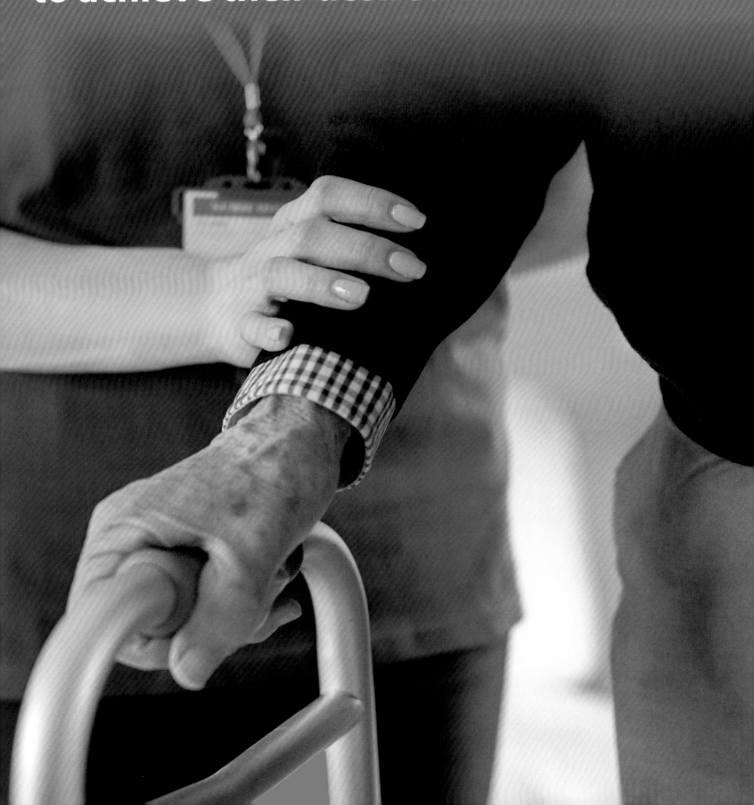

Unit 5

Supporting individuals at risk to achieve their desired outcomes

Unit 5 Introduction: Overview of this Unit

Supporting individuals at risk to achieve their desired outcomes

The purpose of this unit is to gain knowledge and understanding of:

- factors that affect the behaviour of adults
- perspectives affecting adult behaviour
- strategies and approaches that support adults to develop positive behaviour patterns
- factors that could contribute to individuals being at risk of abuse and neglect
- the requirement of legislation, regulation, and codes of conduct for safeguarding and protecting individuals at risk in health and social care
- approaches to securing the rights of individuals. and promoting the rights of individuals

Assessment

This is a non-exam assessment (NEA) made up of two tasks; both of these relate to stimulus materials included within an assessment pack provided via the WJEC secure website on the first Monday in September each year. Both assessment tasks require learners to draw on their knowledge and understanding of supporting individuals at risk to achieve their desired outcomes.

The tasks for this NEA will remain the same for the lifetime of the specification, and are as published in the sample assessment material available from the WJEC secure website.

The assessment contributes 25% of the overall qualification grade of the Diploma. All questions are compulsory, and candidates should be familiar with all the specification content, which will be assessed by the three assessment objectives:

Assessment objective (AO)	% of allocated marks
AO1 – Demonstrate knowledge and understanding of a range of key concepts, values and issues that are related to health and social care.	30-34%
AO2 – Apply knowledge and understanding of health and social care principles and contexts.	33-37%
AO3 – Analyse and evaluate health and social care theories and practice to demonstrate understanding, reflecting on their influence.	31-35%

Areas of content

When studying Unit 5, you may be assessed on all or some of the following five areas of specification content:

Assessment content mapping	Chapter details
5.1 Factors that could contribute to individuals being at risk of abuse and neglect.	Chapter 1 What does 'individuals at risk of abuse and neglect' mean? What are the factors that increase the risk of individuals being at risk of abuse and neglect? Assessment practice based on the sample assessment material questions.
5.2 Factors that can affect the rights of individuals at risk in health and social care.	Chapter 2 What factors could affect the rights of individuals at risk in health and social care? Assessment practice based on the sample assessment material questions.
5.3 The requirements of legislation, regulation, and codes of conduct/practice for safeguarding and protecting individuals at risk in Wales and the UK.	Chapter 3 Legislation, regulation, and codes of conduct/practice for safeguarding and protecting children at risk. Legislation, regulation, and codes of conduct/practice for safeguarding and protecting adults who may be at risk. Assessment practice based on the sample assessment material questions.
5.4 Approaches to securing the rights of individuals at risk in health and social care.	Chapter 4 The practices and approaches that secure the rights of individuals at risk in health and social care. Assessment practice based on the sample assessment material questions.
5.5 The ways in which individual workers and the services they provide can promote inclusion.	Chapter 5 How can individual workers in health and social care promote and make the services they provide more inclusive? Assessment practice based on the sample assessment material questions.

Tasks: Sample assessment materials
(available on the WJEC qualifications website)

You can choose how to present the information, which can be in a table format.

You should spend approximately five hours completing this task.
Total marks (Task 1 and Task 2): 100 marks

The case study context will change annually, but the tasks set will remain the same.

Introduction to the assessment

Through this assessment, you will demonstrate knowledge and understanding gained through the completion of Unit 5: Supporting individuals at risk to achieve their desired outcomes. You will also draw on your knowledge and understanding gained through the completion of Unit 3: Promoting the rights of individuals across the lifespan.

The assessment

In this assessment, you will be required to prepare your response to the following case study of an individual named as PB in this profile. This profile is a profile of an individual at risk.

PROFILE OF PB

PB has been known to Children's Services for many years and has been supported by a wide range of health and social care workers and services. He was adopted at 2 years old after sustaining physical abuse within the home. His birth mother had a drug addiction and his birth father died when he was very young. His birth mother entered a new relationship with a male who physically abused PB.

By the age of 11, PB began to misbehave both at school and at home. He started skipping school and became involved in petty crime and shoplifting. His adoptive parents were unaware of how to manage and support their son. PB has since stated that he was punished at home and these punishments

became increasingly severe over time. In response PB became very upset and aggressive, and his behaviour further deteriorated.

At the age of 15, PB received a custodial sentence at a Youth Offender Institution (YOI). PB had stolen multiple times from the family home, including personal possessions and jewellery. PB was assigned a female social worker because it was felt that it would benefit PB and help him feel less threatened. During this time, PB started to use racist language. When questioned on this, PB informed his social worker that he had overheard support workers using similar remarks and had thought that this was acceptable.

At the age of 16, PB was released on license and returned to his adoptive parents' home. PB's parents helped him when he was released with support from the youth offending team, the local authority and third sector to secure an unpaid work placement. Now aged 17, has, with the help of a Multi-Disciplinary Team (MDT) including his social worker, a psychiatrist, and a counsellor, processed the events that happened in his past and understands how they have contributed to his current situation. He has successfully completed the unpaid work placement and is hoping to gain a place on a motor vehicle apprenticeship in a local further education college. He is currently living in supported living accommodation, receiving support from supported living staff in developing his independent living skills. PB would like to move into social housing, however, his social worker still has concerns over how well he would cope and manage a tenancy. He does not currently have any contact with his birth mother or adoptive parents; however, he has expressed interest in making contact with them in the future.

Task 1	**[66 marks]**

Sample assessment material (SAM)

You are a trainee social worker, supporting the social worker who has been working with PB for many years. He has asked you to prepare up-to-date case notes as PB transitions to the next phase of his life. You have been asked to present your case notes to your Multi-disciplinary Team (MDT) colleagues to ensure a successful transition and lead to positive outcomes.

Case notes are a record of interactions, observations, and actions, and are specific detailed records of information related to any given individual. Designed to record and help pass on detailed information to the next social worker, they are also used to communicate with other professionals who may be involved with an individual's case.

Your case notes should be in the form of a presentation, and should include detailed written notes to clearly evidence the following:

(a) An explanation of the factors that contributed to the individual being at risk of abuse and neglect in the past.   **[20 marks]**

Band AO2: Apply knowledge and understanding of health and social care principles and contexts.

Highest mark band to award 17–20 marks: An excellent response which provides a detailed and coherent explanation of the factors that contributed to the individual being at risk of abuse and neglect in the past. The response demonstrates thorough knowledge and understanding that is consistently applied to the context of the task.

(b) Outline of any current risks of abuse and neglect that need to be communicated to the social services and the MDT.   **[5 marks]**

Band AO1: Demonstrate knowledge and understanding of a range of key concepts, values and issues that are relevant to health and social care.

Highest mark band to award 3–5 marks: A very good response which clearly outlines current risks of abuse and neglect that should be communicated to the MDT. The response demonstrates a range of accurate knowledge and understanding relevant to the requirements of the task.

(c) A description of relevant factors that may have affected the rights of the individual at risk when accessing health and social care services in the past.   **[10 marks]**

You will draw on your knowledge and understanding of the rights of individuals, gained through the completion of *Unit 3: Promoting the rights of individuals across the lifespan.*

Band AO1: Demonstrate knowledge and understanding of a range of key concepts, values and issues that are relevant to health and social care.

Highest mark band to award 8–10 marks: An excellent response which provides a detailed and coherent description of relevant factors that affected the rights of the individual at risk when accessing health and social care services in the past. The response demonstrates detailed and accurate knowledge and understanding relevant to the requirements of the task.

(d) An explanation of current relevant factors that may impact the individual in achieving positive outcomes in the future. **[13 marks]**

Band AO2: Apply knowledge and understanding of health and social care principles and contexts.

Highest mark band to award 11–13 marks: An excellent response which provides a detailed and coherent explanation of current relevant factors that may impact the individual achieving positive outcomes in the future. The response demonstrates detailed and accurate knowledge and understanding relevant to the requirements of the task.

(e) Suggestions of ways in which the health and social care workers identified in the profile, and the services they provide, can promote inclusion for the individual at risk. **[18 marks]**

Band AO1: Demonstrate knowledge and understanding of a range of key concepts, values and issues that are relevant to health and social care.

Highest mark band to award 16–18 marks: An excellent response which provides detailed and coherent suggestions of ways in which health and social care workers in the profile provide services and promote inclusion for the individual at risk. Answer will be wide-ranging in scope. The response demonstrates thorough knowledge and understanding that is consistently applied to the context of the task.

Task 2	**[34 marks]**

As a high-risk individual, it is important to ensure that any future health and social care workers safeguard and protect the individual at risk. To do this, and to support PB's successful progression, you are required to produce information to contribute to a personal care and support plan to assist him through his phase of transition to promote successful outcomes. The information must include:

(a) Examination of how relevant legislation and codes of conduct/practice safeguard and protect the individual at risk.   **[16 marks]**

Band AO3: Analyse and evaluate health and social care principles and contexts to demonstrate understanding, including any influence on practice, making reasoned judgements, and drawing conclusions.

Highest mark band to award 14–16 marks: An excellent response, providing a detailed and insightful examination which:

- ■ makes clear and accurate reference to both relevant legislation and codes of conduct/practice.

- ■ demonstrates a confident grasp of how legislation and codes of conduct/practice safeguard and protect the individual at risk.

- ■ The response demonstrates consistent and appropriate analysis and evaluation skills used in an effective way.

(b) An assessment of how health and social care practices can safeguard individuals, and how approaches can be used to secure the rights of the individual at risk.   **[18 marks]**

Band AO3: Analyse and evaluate health and social care principles and contexts to demonstrate understanding, including any influence on practice, making reasoned judgements, and drawing conclusions.

Highest mark band to award 16–18 marks: An excellent response which provides a detailed and persuasive assessment of:

- ■ how health and social care practices can safeguard individuals.

- ■ how approaches could be used to secure the rights of the individual at risk.

- ■ The response demonstrates consistent and appropriate analysis/ evaluation skills used in an effective way.

Guidance for the assessment

You will have 15 hours in total to complete the assessment, allowing up to 10 hours for writing/typing your response. All internet research is undertaken before commencing the assessment.

You must choose one case study (A or B) to provide your evidence for Task 1 and Task 2. The same case study must be used for both tasks.

Task 1

You will need to prepare up-to-date case notes based on either Case Study A or Case Study B. Your case notes must be based on supporting individuals at risk to achieve their desired outcomes. You should spend approximately 10 hours on this task. You may use the following resources when completing this task:

- ICT software

- Case studies

- Class notes. These should consist of a maximum of six sides of A4 paper. They may be handwritten or word-processed. They should be in your own words, and must not include pre-written answers. Your tutor/assessor is responsible for reviewing the notes to ensure they are within the guidance above.

All notes used during the assessment will be retained by the centre. You are not allowed access to the internet whilst completing this task.

Task 2

You are required to produce information to contribute to a personal care and support plan based on either Case Study A or Case Study B. Your case notes must be based on supporting individuals at risk to achieve their desired outcomes. You should spend approximately five hours on this task.

 You may use the following resources when completing this task:

- ICT software

- Case studies

- Class notes. These should consist of a maximum of six sides of A4 paper. The class notes may be handwritten or typed. They should be your own words and they should not include pre-written answers.

Your tutor/assessor is responsible for reviewing the notes to ensure they are within the guidance above. You are allowed access to the internet while completing this task.

5.1: Factors that could contribute to individuals being at risk of abuse and neglect

The Social Services and Well-being (Wales) Act 2014 defines an **individual at risk** as a person who is experiencing, or is at risk of, abuse, neglect, or other kinds of harm; and has need of care and support.

Key terms

Neglect: failure to provide proper care, such as not providing water to drink.

Abuse: an action deliberately intended to cause harm or distress. It is the mistreatment of an individual by one or more people **which violates his or her civil, legal or human rights.** Abuse can take many forms and affects the service user, their family and even the wider community.

The difference between neglect and abuse: an example of neglect is failing to leave a drink within reach of a service user, while abuse is deliberately leaving a drink out of reach of the service user.

Human rights: these are the principles of human behaviours expected of everyone, regardless of nationality, sex/gender, ethnic origin, place of residence or religion.

Civil rights: the right to political and social freedom and equality, such as the right to free speech (supports the promotion of human rights).

Legal rights: these are rules set out by the legal system, such as the protection of the person or their property (for example: stealing is a crime).

Act of omission: failing to provide something which the service user needs, such as their medication.

Controlling behaviour: domination and manipulation of an individual.

Coercive behaviour: manipulation of an individual by another, usually through threats.

Disempower: make a person or group less confident or less likely to succeed.

Types of abuse

Abuse is cruelty, violence or invasive behaviour inflicted on someone by another person. Abusers can cause physical, sexual, psychological, or emotional harm. Anyone, of any age, gender, race or background, can be a victim of abuse.

Type	Examples	Potential indicators
Physical abuse	Hitting, slapping, over- or misuse of medication, undue restraint, or inappropriate sanctions.	A reluctance to undress in front of others, multiple or minor bruising in different areas with inconsistent and differing explanations, broken bones, bruising to wrists, indicating forced restraint.
Sexual abuse	Rape, sexual assault, or sexual acts which the vulnerable adult has not consented to was pressured into consenting to.	Sexually transmitted diseases, inappropriate conversations of a sexual nature, depression, torn clothes, self-harm/self-neglect, injury, bleeding, and irritation of the genitalia.
Psychological abuse	Threats of harm or abandonment, coercive control, humiliation, verbal or racial abuse, isolation, withdrawal from services or support networks.	Withdrawal and disinterest, avoidance of contact with others, low self-esteem, unusual weight gain or loss, self-isolation, unexplained fearfulness, and anxiety, especially about being alone with particular individuals.
Financial abuse	In relation to individuals who have needs in terms of care and support – theft of money/possessions, misuse of an individual's benefits.	Unexpected change to their will, sudden sale of the home, bills remaining unpaid, complaints that personal property is missing, giving a substantial gift to a carer or other third party.
Neglect	Failure to access medical care or services, negligence in the face of risk-taking, failure to give prescribed medication, failure to assist in personal hygiene or the provision of food, shelter, clothing, emotional neglect.	Personal hygiene concerns, missed appointments, malnourished and dehydrated, pressure sores.

The factors that could contribute to individuals being at risk to abuse and neglect are:

Factor putting an individual at risk	Details
Carer stress	The carer may feel under pressure and unable to cope with looking after the service user.
Dependency	Certain groups are more vulnerable, such as children, older individuals, individuals living with disabilities (physical, cognitive impairment), since they rely or depend on others for care and support.
Family conflict	Individuals who have experienced childhood abuse or domestic violence may believe that this is acceptable behaviour.
Isolation	Individuals who are socially isolated, without access to support or information about how they can be protected.
Medical/ psychological conditions	Individuals with low self-confidence and self-esteem, communication difficulties and mental illness may not be able or willing to complain about what is happening.
Other factors	■ **Religious beliefs**: set rules that must be followed and respected, so if individuals break these rules, there may be consequences, which could include all types of abuse and neglect. For example, in some religions, it is made clear about what an individual's sexual orientation should be, as well as the acceptable codes of dress and behaviour. For some religious/cultural beliefs, the risk of a **forced marriage** is greater, and could be a contributing factor to individuals being at risk. (It is important to distinguish between a forced marriage and an arranged marriage; a **forced marriage** is where individuals are made to marry without giving consent, whereas an **arranged marriage** is when both individuals consent). ■ **Race**: racist abuse and harassment are forms of direct discrimination. ■ **Sexuality orientation/differences** produce discrimination in employment and training: it is illegal for an employer to discriminate because of a person's sexuality. Individuals could face hate crimes; there could be psychological abuse by being threatened with the exposure of their sexual orientation. ■ **Substance misuse** of alcohol or drugs can contribute to individuals being at risk of abuse or neglect. ■ **Position in family**: children in a family may be treated differently, according to being the oldest or youngest, or a stepchild, for example. ■ **Scapegoating**: this is a common form of parental verbal abuse, where individuals are blamed for all the problems in a dysfunctional household; they can also be scapegoated by friends and local community. ■ **Lack of awareness, training or monitoring of workers to spot or deal with safeguarding issues**: this could lead to neglect and abuse continuing, leading to further damage, and even death of the victim.

Some individuals are more vulnerable and at risk of abuse and neglect:

Type of vulnerability	Description according to P.I.E.S. (Physical, Intellectual, Emotional, Social)
Physical vulnerability	The individual may have a chronic medical condition, such as arthritis, or may have become physically weaker with age, so movement and mobility may be slower. Children are usually shorter and lighter than adults, and therefore they are more vulnerable to physical abuse.
Intellectual/ cognitive vulnerability	An individual having difficulty remembering, concentrating, and learning or making decisions can be more vulnerable to abuse, exploitation, or neglect. The causes of this impairment could be a head injury, damage to the brain following a stroke, or being born with learning disabilities. Disabled adults and children are more dependent on others to look after them, so they are vulnerable.
Emotional vulnerability	Psychologically, the individual often thinks they are in some way inferior to, or not as worthy as other people, and may be unable or unwilling to complain about what is happening to them. An individual with depression, anxiety or phobias may react differently to the dangers around them and may be more vulnerable to persuasion or coercion.
Social vulnerability	The individual is unable to deal with negative events in their life and can be lonely for a range of reasons; older people may outlive their friends and relatives and lose confidence in making new friends; new parents who are coping with a baby may feel socially isolated and vulnerable, as may children who have moved from one home to another.

Activity 1

Discussion: Why is it important to be aware of the reasons for an individual's vulnerability when trying to minimise the risk of abuse or neglect?

Discussion: Identify four possible reasons for a carer to become stressed.

Reasons for family conflict

- **Parenting styles** – some parents have an extremely strict, authoritarian parenting style, placing high expectations on children and focusing more on obedience, discipline, and control rather than nurture. Authoritarian parents expect the child not to make mistakes and to obey them, which can lead to child neglect and abuse.

- **Financial constraints** – families who are struggling financially may be stressed and, as a result, take out their frustrations and lack of control on others.

- **New family members, e.g. baby, pets**. A baby may change the family relationships, causing greater anxiety and stress, and family members may get jealous due to a lack of attention.

- **Health difficulties** – a family member who is living with health difficulties may need more support, and this may result in carer stress.

- **Substance misuse in the home** – if family members are drinking excessively or taking drugs, this will affect their behaviour and may result in potential harm for other members of the household.

■ **A lot of family abuse and neglect goes unreported because of the family circle of abuse**: individuals who witnessed or experienced domestic abuse as a child are more likely to be abused by a partner; this may be because this behaviour has been **normalised.** Therefore, the individual views abuse as normal and these behaviour patterns are **imitated,** which means behaviour is copied.

A note of caution with any statistics regarding family abuse and conflict is that **statistics only measure the abuse and neglect that have been detected and reported** – lots of family abuse and neglect goes undetected and never ends up in statistical data.

Many individuals may not report abuse and neglect within the family due to a number of reasons:

1   They do not know they suffered abuse and neglect.

2   They may lack the self-confidence to report abuse and neglect within the family.

3   They may not want to get their parents or guardians into trouble, or fear the consequences of reporting.

When supporting individuals who may be at risk to abuse and neglect, it is important to understand what abuse and neglect means to an individual who is brought up in a family where abuse is an intrinsic part of their everyday life. The Welsh Government has responded to these situations and to the variety of reasons that can lead to family conflict. It has prepared a methodology to measure well-being throughout Wales, in addition to providing legislation, codes of practice and a procedures framework so that vulnerable individuals can feel that they are safe and protected from abuse and neglect.

The causes of family conflict

Did you know …

- By building a positive relationship/rapport with the service user, health and social care workers can get a better understanding of "what matters to them"; they have a better chance of knowing that something may not be right, and that they may be at risk or experiencing abuse and neglect.

- Children and young people who have disabilities are at an increased risk of being abused compared with their non-disabled peers, and are also less likely to receive the protection and support they need when they have been abused. Individuals who have additional learning needs have the right to have information that is accessible so that they can have a voice and exercise choice and control regarding their care and support.

- Validity of data: statistics regarding abuse may not be valid, since there could be lots of cases that go undetected or not reported.

- There are codes of practice (standards/rules) that health and social care workers are required to follow. One practice that social care workers must follow is that they are not allowed to take presents or money from individuals they support, including unpaid carers; this ensures that individuals who are at risk can live safely and free from any abuse.

- Neglect by health and social care workers is not always a deliberate act; sometimes it can happen due to a lack of awareness or training/monitoring. However, whether deliberate or not, neglect can have serious health consequences for the individual service user. Training and experience can raise staff awareness of how to avoid or spot potential signs that individuals may be at risk of, or experiencing, neglect. Also, identifying individuals who may be at risk of neglect early on, could prevent neglect from escalating, which could improve their overall health outcomes.

- Abuse and neglect can happen in any setting, whether it is in an individual's home, an institution, or any other place. In September 2020, Yew Trees Hospital was closed after a formal inspection found evidence of abuse of the vulnerable adult patients. Unfortunately, these are not isolated incidents – there have been other incidents of health and social care settings with a culture of abusing and neglecting the individuals that they should be caring for and supporting.

- ■ **Some older individuals and other individuals living with disabilities may need home care, or even need to move into residential care due to a range of factors, including**:

  - being unable to safely live within their home due to a change of circumstances, including ageing, cognitive impairments, accidents, death of family members, or family members/carers who are unable to meet the needs of the individual.

  - the local authority have already completed a care and needs assessment, and have suggested that residential care or nursing care is the best choice to meet the needs of the individual, as they have complex medical conditions. This includes possible cognitive impairments, needing specialist staff support for 24 hours, 7 days a week. (Cognitive impairments are when individuals have difficulty remembering, learning new things, concentrating, communicating, retaining information, and making decisions that affect their everyday lives).

- ■ **Health and social care workers** are monitored and inspected by Care Inspectorate Wales and Healthcare Inspectorate Wales. Although these inspectorates have robust inspection systems, some abuse and neglect can go undetected, especially if health and social care workers are not monitored effectively within their own organisation.

  Unpaid carers are not monitored by Care Inspectorate Wales and Healthcare Inspectorate Wales. This could lead to individuals being at a greater risk of abuse and neglect within the domestic setting.

Activity 2

Sharon is a care worker; she provides care and support to Jean who is 65 years old. Jean has limited mobility following a stroke.

Explain how Jean's situation could make her vulnerable to financial abuse.

Reading and further research:

Research (2014) into sexual abuse **https://socialcare.wales/cms_assets/file-uploads/10a-CSE.pdf**

Working Together to Safeguard People **https://www.socialcare.wales/hub/statutory-guidance**

BBC 2019 Report on abuse **https://www.bbc.co.uk/news/uk-wales-49418681**

Resource for supporting older adults who may be at risk of abuse or experiencing abuse **https://olderpeople.wales/**

Carer stress **https://www.bbc.co.uk/news/uk-wales-49418681**

Supporting older adults who may be at risk of abuse or experiencing abuse **https://olderpeople.wales/**

The Hate Crime (2017) report which highlights some of the abuse and neglect that individuals have faced because of their sexual orientation. **https://www.childline.org.uk/info-advice/your-feelings/sexual-identity/sexual-orientation**

ACTIVITY ANSWER
Activity 2 – Jean

- ◼ Jean may not be able to leave the house without assistance to access banking. Therefore, she may:
  - be more likely to give her banking information to others
  - keep her money in the house.

- ◼ Jean may no longer have the ability to be able to understand money and finances, which could make her vulnerable to:
  - scams
  - being manipulated by others.

5.2: Factors that can affect the rights of individuals at risk in health and social care

Who are 'individuals at risk to abuse and neglect'?

Individuals identified as **at risk** are referred to as being **vulnerable**. The Social Services and Well-being (Wales) Act 2014 makes a distinction between an adult at risk and a child at risk:

- a '**child at risk**' is a child who is experiencing, or is at risk of, abuse, neglect or other kinds of harm, and needs care and support (whether or not the local authority is meeting any of those needs). A child is considered to be an individual under the age of 18.

- an '**adult at risk**' involves three aspects: an adult who is experiencing, or is at risk of, abuse and neglect; needs care and support (whether or not the local authority is meeting any of those needs), and as a result of those needs, is unable to protect himself, or herself, against the abuse or neglect or the risk of it. An adult is considered to be an individual over the age of 18.

Factors that can affect the rights of individuals at risk in health and social care

Individuals have certain rights regarding the healthcare treatment they receive. This includes not being discriminated against in any way, and receiving the information the person requires. The acronyms ACCURACY and LIPS can be used to remember the 12 factors that can affect the rights of individuals using health and social care services.

A.C.C.U.R.A.C.Y.	L.I.P.S.
Attitudes of individuals working in settings that promote person-centred care	**L**ack of advocacy
Capacity to understand information or to decide	**I**solation
Communication ability	**P**ersonal traits of individuals who are accessing outcome-focused person-centred care and support
Understanding their rights as an individual according to their age	**S**upporting family and carers' input and awareness of the rights of the individual
Recognising that carers have the right to be supported	
Availability of resources	
Conflict between the rights of individuals and the views of the families and health and social care workers	
Young carers' support services	

1. Attitudes of health and social care workers

- Poor attitude: if a member of staff mistreats and discriminates against some service users or does not promote person-centred care.

- If the workers have had little training or limited work experience in the health and social care sector, they may not be able to communicate effectively with individuals who have any complex communication needs.

- Workers may not be able to identify and change environmental barriers negatively affecting communication, such as a loud background noise.

- Person-centred care should focus on the holistic needs of individuals by concentrating on the individual as a whole, rather than just on that individual's specific needs, such as their medical needs; this enables the individual service user to be an equal partner in their care.

Other examples of unacceptable worker attitudes may result from their prejudices/ discrimination:

Racism: treating another person differently because of the colour of their skin being different to theirs, speaking a different language, having different religious/cultural views/beliefs.

Sexism: stereotyped views of the role of a male and a female; believing them to be superior or inferior to one another.

Ageism: stereotyping older/younger people, showing prejudice and discrimination because of their age.

How can an individual's sexual orientation lead to being at risk of abuse and neglect?

- Individuals can face **homophobia**: negative attitudes and feelings toward homosexuality, or people identified, or perceived as being homosexual/gay.

- Individuals could face **conversion therapy**, or be pressurised to question their sexuality.

2. Capacity of service users to understand (Service user's cognitive capacity)

- Individuals with drug or alcohol addictions; even those who have had their drinks spiked on a night out can be classed as vulnerable.

- Individuals with mental ill health (including dementia), or reduced cognitive ability, may find some difficulty in making decisions.

- Individuals with learning difficulties or disabilities (additional learning needs).

- Individuals who live with cognitive impairments may be dependent on others for care and support. Individuals with cognitive impairments have difficulty remembering, learning new things, concentrating, communicating, making decisions regarding that affect their everyday life, and retaining information.

There are a number of cognitive impairments, including:

- **Alzheimer's disease** is a common type of dementia in the UK. It is an ongoing decline of cognitive functioning and can affect thought processes.

- **Vascular dementia** is a type of dementia caused by a reduced blood flow to the brain.

- **Corticiobasal degeneration** (CBD) is a rare condition that gradually worsens to create problems with movement, speech and swallowing.

- **Huntington's disease** is caused by a faulty gene in the DNA which affects the body's nervous system, causing problems with movement, as well as with emotional health and well-being.

- **Mild cognitive impairment** is when an individual has minor problems with their cognition, memory and thinking. This would mean that these conditions would be worse than expected in a healthy individual at their age.

- **Primary progressive aphasia** is caused by damage to parts of the brain that control language, personality and emotions, so individuals have difficult expressing words.

- **Progressive supranuclear palsy** is a rare progressive condition that can cause problems with balance, mobility, vision, speech, and swallowing.

- **Parkinson's disease** is a condition when parts of the brain become progressively damaged over a period of time. This condition can lead to involuntary movements, less movement, and stiff and inflexible muscles, as well as causing speech difficulties.

In order to make a decision, some adults at risk may require additional support, such as advocacy services, providing simplified explanations, supplying visual aids and giving additional time. Patients are legally entitled to receive this support.

If individuals lack capacity to understand information or to make a decision, it is important that any act or decision made on behalf of an 'individual at risk' is made in their **best interests**.

3. Communication ability

The ability to communicate is restricted due to the loss of hearing, speech or vision difficulties, which make effective communication more difficult.

Factors that could affect the communication abilities of individuals at risk:

- **Communication barriers:** such as cognitive impairments, learning disabilities (additional learning needs), language barriers.

- **Isolation:** individuals not able to access information, as they are not able to communicate their needs. Individuals may also have poor access to services, so do not have a chance to communicate their needs to the appropriate care and support networks.

- **Physical and mental health:** individuals may be living with a mental illness and are lacking in self-confidence, so they may easily conceal their problems. Individuals may also have physical difficulties, and may not have the opportunity to communicate their needs to others.

- **Lack of status/social exclusion:** as a result of being at risk, they may lack status, and may not have the confidence to communicate to seek care and support.

4. Understanding their rights as service users according to their age

Some older or younger individuals may not be aware of, or understand their rights.

Older adults may have additional support and care needs.

Individuals at risk have rights to protect them. These individuals are legally entitled to these rights, which are embedded in various pieces of legislation, such as the Social Services Well-being (Wales) Act 2014, the Children Act 2004 and the Equality Act 2010.

When supporting individuals at risk, health and social care workers also have to ensure that they act in a way which is compatible with their rights under the European Convention of Human Rights. Care Inspectorate Wales have established training sessions so that staff provide patients and clients in Wales with high-quality social care. During their visits to various settings, they will also monitor whether the following individual rights are being followed within the setting.

These include that:

- individuals have choice and control
- each individual is safe
- everyone is treated with respect and dignity

■ all individuals have a right to be heard

■ every individual is helped to develop to their full potential.

The Social Services and Well-being (Wales) Act 2014 also gives individuals more say about the type of care and support they receive. This enables individuals to understand what options they have ,which is a vital part of this legislation, alongside individuals having the right to be heard, including a right to express concerns and complaints. If an individual is not aware of their rights, this could result in them feeling disempowered and not an **equal partner** in any care and support that is being offered.

5. Recognition of carers' rights

■ The family/carer must have their own rights protected so that they can meet the specific needs of the individual.

Carers have the right to:

■ their **well-being**

■ have **information**, **advice** and **assistance** as required

■ have an **assessment** if their needs cannot be met by just providing information and advice

■ have their **voice** heard and to be able to have **control over decisions** about the support they require.

6. Availability of resources

- Resources such as workers, clinics, care homes, day care centres or transport to appointments may not be available.

- Health and social care workers may not have enough time to provide quality care. This may be due to a number of reasons, such as timed visits, or being tired and overworked, resulting in potential abuse and neglect.

- Health and social care workers and unpaid carers may experience high levels of stress, and this may lead to neglect or abuse.

- If health and social care workers are not able to identify or deal with any safeguarding issues, this may result in individuals being at greater risk of harm.

7. Conflict between the service user and their family or their carers

- An example is when the service user wishes to live more independently in their own separate home, but the family do not want this to happen.

- Family conflict puts individuals more at risk of abuse and neglect – this could include individuals who have experienced childhood abuse, or domestic violence, and they may believe that this behaviour is acceptable.

8. Young carers support services

- Many children and young people are carers for a parent or sibling, and should receive support with their role. Sometimes, there are young carers' groups available to offer support, advice and guidance, so that the young person does not feel alone in their role as a carer.

- The local authority has a **duty to assess**, and must ensure that the ability of the young carer is **sustainable**, and that the carer's well-being is promoted alongside that of the individual that they care for. Young carers may also have **care and support plans** drawn up to support their **well-being**. In the care and support plan, the local authority must have regard to the developmental needs of the young carer, and must be inclusive by using appropriate language which will enable the young carer to participate fully in the planning process. In this way, young carers will have a voice, and can exercise choice and control over any services which may be available to support them. Care and support plans must have a review date and must not exceed six months.

9. Lack of advocacy

Advocacy means getting support from another person to help express an individual's views and wishes, and to help them to stand up for their rights. An advocate can support individual service users by:

- listening to views and concerns
- helping them to explore options and rights, without pressurising the person
- providing information to help make informed decisions
- helping to find contact details of relevant people such as health and social care professionals, or to contact them on their behalf
- accompanying and supporting them in meetings or appointments.

An advocate should not:

- give their personal opinion
- decide and make decisions for the individual
- make judgements about the individual.

A lack of advocacy can result in individuals being at greater risk of abuse and neglect due to:

- potentially not having outcomes, or changes that the individual wants to make to their lives
- not understanding the behaviour of others, who are abusive and neglectful
- not being aware of what actions they can take to safeguard themselves
- not being aware of their rights
- not being supported through the safeguarding process.

10. Isolation

- An individual may become, or choose to become, socially isolated and is unable to access support networks.
- They may lack access to information, advocacy, and support in relation to how they can be protected.
- Isolation often affects groups who are discriminated against, such as because of their ethnicity, sexuality, or age.
- Individuals who are socially excluded may not feel they are valued in society, and as a result, do not have self-worth and a sense of belonging; they may not have the confidence to access support networks, resulting in not voicing their concerns over being in danger or harmed.
- These individuals may not have information about support groups that can help safeguard and protect them.

11. Personal characteristics

Individuals living with mental illnesses may be at risk of abuse and neglect, since they feel powerless, and may just accept that abuse and neglect. Individuals who live with mental illnesses may depend on others for care and support, and this care and support may be extremely demanding. Health and social care workers and unpaid carers may experience high levels of stress, and this may lead to abuse, including psychological abuse.

12. Supporting family and carers in raising awareness of their rights

Carers and the family of the patient or client may also be vulnerable and at risk of abuse or neglect. They also have the right to be kept safe from harm and abuse.

Young carers may have **care and support plans** drawn up alongside those of family members, in order to support their **well-being**. Young carers have the right to a local authority assessment, to see if the authority can offer care and support.

The local authority has a duty to assess to ensure that the abilities and capabilities of the young carer can be **sustained**, and that their well-being is promoted, alongside that of the individual they care for.

Activity 1

CASE STUDY – MARI

Mari is 17 years old, and cares for and supports her mother Alison and her stepmother Deborah. She attends college three times a week, and is supported by a welfare officer at the college. Mari wants to remain at college and become a British Army soldier. Alison and Deborah both live with depression, and have mobility needs, so they are dependent on Mari to provide care and support. Mari supports both her parents by waking them up every morning, preparing and giving them their anti-depressants. Mari prepares their breakfast and lunch, before helping them down the stairs and heading off to college.

On her return from college, she does all the housework, which includes cleaning the dishes, washing, preparing tea, and making sure both women have been given their second dose of anti-depressants later that evening. Mari helps both parents back up to bed, before finishing any outstanding assessment tasks she has to complete.

Recently, she has been invited to attend a four-day training course, but this would require Mari to stay away for three nights. Mari is unsure how her parents would cope if she attended the training course.

1. Define the term **young carer**, and give reasons why Mari should be classed as a young carer.

2. Give **two** reasons why Alison and Deborah may be at risk of abuse and neglect.

3. Why is the risk of abuse and/or neglect greater in some care settings?

4. Research and prepare a list of the support services available for young carers in your local area.

Advocacy

Types of advocacies

- **Self-advocacy**: an individual represents themselves, speaking up for themself and their concerns.

- **Group advocacy**: a group presentation with a common goal; special interest groups or pressure groups.

- **Collective advocacy**: when a group of people with similar experiences get together to raise issues and try to get changes in place.

- **Peer advocacy**: one-to-one support provided by other individuals with a similar disability/experience.

- **Informal advocacy**: involves family, friends, and unpaid advocates.

- **Citizen advocacy**: involves fully trained volunteers who act as advocates for local people, such as at Citizens Advice.

- **Formal advocacy**: organisations pay their staff to advocate for someone, or for a group of individuals.

Independent professional advocacy involves trained professional advocates paid for their work.

▲ Advocacy services as described in the Social Services and Well-being (Wales) Act 2014, Part 10 Code of Practice (Advocacy). © Age Cymru.

Some professional advocacy services available to individuals at risk

SEAP: **S**upport, **E**mpower, **A**dvocate, **P**romote is an independent charity specialising in the provision of advocacy and related services.

Citizens Advice: Citizens Advice provides general support, and can provide advocacy services.

MENCAP: UK charity representing people living with a learning disability, and also their families and carers.

NSPCC: National Society for the Prevention of Cruelty to Children; provides help for children who have been abused, or are at risk of being abused or neglected.

Social Services: local authority service providers.

POhWER: A UK charity helping people to become involved in decisions about their care. They focus on ensuring that voices are heard and that lives are empowered.

An **Independent Mental Capacity Advocate (IMCA)** service provides an advocate, appointed to act on behalf of a person if they lack capacity to make certain decisions. Independent mental capacity advocates will represent individuals, and contribute to 'best-interest' assessments, under the Mental Capacity Act 2005. IMCAs are appointed in Wales by a local Health Board or other NHS body.

In England, IMCAs are appointed by a local authority, and in Wales, they are appointed by a local Health Board or other NHS body in Wales.

Activity 2

CASE STUDY – DR MORENO

Dr Moreno has supported several individuals at the hospital today:

- ■ **Callum** (9 years old), who lives with autism and suffers from earaches.
- ■ **Linda** (37 years old), who lives with mental illness and hearing impairment.
- ■ **Carla** (57 years old), who has been drinking alcohol excessively, and during the day.
- ■ **Granville** (79 years old), who lives with a heart condition and a cognitive impairment known as corticiobasal degeneration (a rare disease causing the brain to shrink and nerve cells to degenerate and die over time).

1. Identify the issues facing Callum, Linda, Carla, and Granville when communicating with the staff at the hospital.

2. Suggest, using examples and ideas, the types of communication styles that Dr Moreno could use to communicate effectively so as to improve the health outcomes for the four individuals who need support.

3. List the factors that impact on the effectiveness of the interaction between Dr Moreno and the individuals being supported.

Reading and further research

Effective communication
https://www.bbc.co.uk/bitesize/topics/zbp2scw

SEAP (Support, Empower, Advocate, Promote) | The Legal Education
Foundation
https://thelegaleducationfoundation.org/

CAP
https://capuk.org/

MENCAP
https://wales.mencap.org.uk/

NSPCC
https://www.nspcc.org.uk/about-us/what-we-do/wales/

POhWER
https://www.pohwer.net/what-is-advocacy

Independent Mental Capacity Advocate (IMCA)
**https://socialcare.wales/qualifications-funding/qualification-
framework/job-roles/advocacy-services/independent-mental-capacity-
advocate**

ACTIVITY ANSWERS
Activity 1 – Mari

1. Define the term 'young carer', and give reasons why Mari should be classed as a young carer.

Mari is a young carer. A young carer is a young person under 18 years of age who is unpaid, and cares for someone with any type of physical or mental illness, disability, or misuse of substances such as alcohol or drugs. As a result of the Social Services Well-being (Wales) Act 2014, young carers have the right to have their well-being promoted and protected through the local authority, which ensures that support services, including information and advice, are accessible in a variety of formats including easy reading material. If these information and advice services are not accessible to young carers, they may not have the opportunity to know what support is available to support their well-being, and also to support the individuals that they are caring for. Young carers have the right to a local authority assessment to see if they can offer care and support. The local authority has a duty to assess, and must ensure that the young carer's abilities can be sustained, and that the carer's well-being is promoted alongside that of the individual they care for.

2. Give two reasons why Alison and Deborah may be at risk of abuse and neglect.

- Alison and Deborah suffer from depression, and rely on support to provide their regular medication.
- Both have additional mobility needs and are dependent on care.
- They need personal care and support to provide food and a clean and safe home.
- Both Alison and Deborah may find it difficult to communicate and to raise awareness of abuse or neglect.
- They have little or no social contact with others to raise any concerns that they may have.
- Poverty and lower social-economic status of some service users may mean that they have less confidence to assert their concerns within the setting.

3. Why is the risk of abuse or/and neglect greater in some care settings?

- Care home services including those who provide care home services for children or adults have regular monitoring and they are inspected by Care Inspectorate Wales. However, domestic settings providing care in a service user's home have a reduced level of scrutiny compared to a care or nursing home. Larger care settings have a larger number of staff and a larger number of visiting professionals, and they are more likely to be aware of abuse or neglect.

- Feedback from service users or their family is encouraged in some settings enabling concerns to be raised sooner rather than later.

- Lack of social support for the service users means difficulty or delays in communicating possible concerns.

- Poverty and lower social-economic status of some service users may mean they have less confidence to assert their concerns within the setting.

ACTIVITY ANSWERS
Activity 2 – Dr Moreno

1. Identify the issues facing Callum, Linda, Carla, and Granville when communicating at the hospital.

Callum (9 years old), who is living with autism, may:

- have difficulty reading social cues and body language

- miss non-verbal cues

- avoid eye contact

- not understand difficult questions

- be sensitive to environmental concerns

- experience anxiety in different and unfamiliar situations, which may result in him not listening, or concentrating on what is being said.

Linda (37 years old), who is living with mental illness and hearing impairment, may:

- not be able to hear very well and not understand instructions, so she may not have any voice, choice, or control over her treatment

- feel worthless due to her mental illness, preventing her from communicating with Dr Moreno about her symptoms

- not have appropriate treatment to meet her needs.

Carla (57 years old), who drinks alcohol excessively throughout the day, may:

- be unable to receive or retain information communicated to her, or she may misinterpret messages in a distorted way.

- not understand what is being said to her, and the alcohol could impact on her mental state, causing her to become frustrated or even angry.

Granville (79 years old), who is living with a heart condition and a cognitive impairment known as corticiobasal degeneration, may:

- have slowed and slurred speech; he also may have speech and language difficulties, and not be able to express his thoughts clearly.

- may experience severe breathing issues due to his heart condition, which will require urgent medical attention.

2. Suggest, using examples, the types of communication techniques that Dr Moreno could use to communicate effectively with the patients or clients, to improve the health outcomes for the four individuals who are being supported.

- Dr Moreno should ensure that she is always speaking clearly, in the language and format of a patient's choice.

- Active listening (verbal/speaking – active listening involves checking for understanding and asking appropriate questions to confirm understanding).

- Ensure that she speaks at a level that individuals can hear.

- She should speak clearly and concisely, at a pace that individuals can understand.

- Use words and medical terminology that individuals can understand. The doctor needs to be careful not to overuse medical jargon.

- Use distraction techniques, such as general conversation (or small talk) to facilitate further conversation.

- Non-verbal: facial expressions need to be clear, alongside eye contact, body language, posture, nodding and hand gestures to show interest.

- Graphical: diagrams could be used to help individuals understand a condition or illness, or to explain a treatment plan.

- Written: records the treatment and any appropriate observation that is witnessed, the consent form should be signed if required.

Callum: Dr Moreno needs to ensure that her language is clear and precise. For example, if she says, "Wash your hands in the toilet", Callum may then actually wash his hands in the toilet – so the instruction needs to be made specific ("Wash your hands in the sink in the toilet"). When Dr Moreno leaves the room, she will need to make sure that she makes clear to Callum what is happening to him, as Callum may not be able to pick up non-verbal cues. Dr Moreno should keep communication focussed and to the point, to explore what matters to Callum, since this can help to build a rapport with him.

Linda: Dr Moreno's body position is important. Dr Moreno should face Linda so she can see the doctor's mouth. Dr Moreno needs to make sure that she has Linda's attention by gently tapping their arm or saying her name. The doctor should try and avoid loud background noise. Linda could also use some aids to help communicate, such as a hearing aid, visual aids, sign language or loop systems. Dr Moreno could build up a positive relationship with Linda, so that she knows what matters to her.

Carla: The doctor needs to make sure that Carla is safe and secure, and that all policies and procedures are followed when communicating with her.

Granville: Dr Moreno needs to speak at a slower pace, allowing time for Granville to process what has been said. If Granville does not understand, she should use objects, images, or hand movements. If Granville changes the conversation, then the doctor needs to find a way to return to the initial conversation.

3. List some factors impacting the effectiveness of communication between Dr Moreno and the individuals being supported.

- Environmental factors

- Seating arrangements

- Temperature of room

- Background noise

- Lighting – bright or dark

- Any personal characteristic that could produce ineffective interpersonal interactions.

5.3: The requirements of legislation, regulation, and codes of practice for safeguarding and protecting individuals at risk in Wales and the UK

The most important current requirements for safeguarding include the following legislation, regulations, and codes of practice. It's vitally important that you have a detailed knowledge and understanding of the safeguarding requirements included within the documents.

Social Services and Well-being (Wales) Act 2014

This Act provides the legal framework used for improving the well-being of individuals who need care and support, and also carers who need support. It is also an important cornerstone for transforming social services in Wales. Its purpose is to impose duties on local authorities, health boards and Welsh ministers that will require them to promote the well-being of those individuals who need care and support, or carers who need support.

The Children Act 2004

The Children Act 2004 states that all individuals involved with health and social care and related organisations working with children have a duty of responsibility to help safeguard children and promote child welfare across the UK.

Wales Safeguarding Procedures (2019)

The national Wales Safeguarding Procedures detail the essential roles and responsibilities for practitioners to make certain that they safeguard children and adults who are at risk of abuse and neglect. The Procedures aim to apply the Social Services and Well-being (Wales) Act 2014 legislation. The document also focuses on how to implement the statutory safeguarding guidance *Working Together to Safeguard People*. These Procedures are revised regularly to reflect changes in legislation, guidance, and practice. The procedures provide a guide to safeguarding practice guidelines for health and social care workers and other services. The Procedures provides a framework for delivering standardised safeguarding practice across Wales, and also greater cooperation between agencies.

Welsh Government safeguarding guidance

This safeguarding guidance provides information about the essential roles and responsibilities for practitioners to ensure that they safeguard children and young people and adults who are at risk of abuse and neglect. The safeguarding guidance provides a practical and useful guide to help practitioners apply the Social Services and Well-being (Wales) Act 2014.

Safeguarding – relevant statutory documents:

- For working with children, **Working Together to Safeguard People: Volume 5 – Handling Individual Cases to Protect Children at Risk** is an important part of legislation for children at risk.

- For working with adults at risk, **Working Together to Safeguard People: Volume 6 – Handling Individual Cases to Protect Adults at Risk** provides legislation and regulations.

- Alongside this legislation, it is also important to study **Working Together to Safeguard People: Volume 1 – Introduction and Overview**.

Safeguarding refers to specific measures taken to protect the health, well-being, and the human rights of individuals, especially children, young people, and vulnerable adults to live free from abuse, harm, and neglect.

Key terms

Abuse: this is the act of causing someone distress or harm. Abuse can take many different forms, such as physical or psychological harm, and includes domestic violence, sexual abuse, emotional abuse, financial, material abuse, modern slavery, and discriminatory abuse.

Adult at risk: an individual aged 18 or over who may need community care services due to mental or other disability, age, or illness; and who is, or may be, unable to take care of themselves, or unable to protect themselves against significant harm or exploitation.

Child at risk: an individual aged under 18 who is experiencing or is at risk of abuse, neglect, or other kinds of harm.

Disclosure of abuse: when a child, young person or adult begins to share their safeguarding issues with others. The disclosure can relate to the person telling someone else about the abuse that has taken place or is taking place.

Neglect: is the persistent failure to meet basic physical, emotional and/or psychological needs, likely to result in the serious impairment of an individual's health or development. Neglect may occur during pregnancy because of maternal drugs or substance abuse.

Safeguarding: is the action that an organisation takes to promote the welfare of children and vulnerable adults to protect them from harm, including physical, emotional, sexual, and financial harm and neglect. This includes making sure that the appropriate policies, practices, and procedures are put in place. Organisations working with children and vulnerable adults must do all they can to keep them safe and protected from harm, abuse, or neglect.

Self-determination: is the key difference between safeguarding adults and children. Adults may choose not to act to protect themselves, and it is only in extreme circumstances that the law intervenes. When an adult has the capacity to make decisions for themselves and decides to put themselves at risk, presenting no risk of significant harm to children or to other adults, then their decisions and confidentiality should be maintained.

Legislation: refers to the process of laws being prepared and passed into law by a government. Health and social care organisations and their staff must perform their duties in accordance with the law. The Social Services and Well-being (Wales) Act 2014 includes statutory legislation to provide a legal framework for health and social care workers in terms of what is required by the legislation regarding safeguarding individuals at risk.

Regulation: is a way to make sure that health and social care workers are safe to practise and remain safe throughout their professional career. Regulation provides guidance and rules on how the legislation should be implemented in accordance with the relevant Act. Regulations are also enforceable guidelines that must be followed by health and social care workers delivering services.

Health and social care services in Wales are regulated and inspected by Care Inspectorate Wales and Healthcare Inspectorate Wales. These are organisations that monitor professional areas to ensure individuals in Wales receive excellent quality of care.

In Wales, the **Regulation and Inspection of Social Care (Wales) Act 2016** was set up to protect the well-being of individuals and to keep them safe from abuse and neglect. The **Nursing and Midwifery Council** (NMC) is the professional regulator of nurses, midwives, and nursing associates across the UK, aiming to make sure that health care is safe, effective, and kind for all individuals using the service.

A code of conduct and practice sets the standard of conduct expected of health and social care workers

The **code of conduct and practice** outlines the behaviour and attitudes that an individual can expect to experience from health and social care workers supporting the patient or client's desired outcomes. Codes of conduct and practice act as **guides to deliver best practice and conduct**. They should guide the day-to-day working practices of health and social care workers on how best to safeguard and protect individuals at risk.

A code of conduct and practice gives details on many aspects of care, including details of when **advocacy** should be offered to the service user. The code, for example, describes the conditions and circumstances of when an individual may need advocacy services. Advocacy services provide support from another person to help the individual express their views and wishes, and help the service user to stand up for their rights.

The code of conduct and practice emphasises the importance of **multi-agency working** in providing a coordinated approach where professionals work together to provide a seamless service. This will involve health and social care workers collaborating with other professionals in education, drug and alcohol services, mental health services, housing, probation, and social services.

This collaboration will enable an individual to receive health and care services which draw together the expertise of a family of professionals who will be able to respond to the needs of individuals with multiple and complex health and social care issues. This will involve the expertise of a multi-disciplinary team of professionals.

Ways to protect vulnerable children, young adults and adults include:

- having in place policies and procedures that will help make sure that children and vulnerable adults are protected from harm
- making sure those policies and procedures are implemented and understood by everyone
- having clear lines of responsibility and accountability to deal with any safeguarding issues
- making sure that staff are trained to identify potential harm, know what action to take, and are clear about what, when and how to report.

What actions should be taken if someone witnesses or suspects abuse, harm, or neglect?

Disclosure of abuse is when you witness or suspect abuse, or when someone tells you they are being abused. If this happens, then the health and social worker or whoever has to disclose that information. It is everyone's duty to report abuse, harm, or neglect.

Procedures to be followed include:

- Contact 999 if a child or an adult is in immediate danger.

- The incident or the concern should be reported as soon as possible, as this will ensure that action to safeguard the child or adult will be taken sooner. Details of the event will also be sharper and more accurate. It's important to speak out to report all concerns.

- The details have to be reported to a relevant person within the organisation. Details of the person to contact will be included within the safeguarding handbook of the organisation.

- An official record has to be prepared to record the incident or the concern.

- The organisation has a duty of care to make enquiries or to investigate an incident or a concern about the safety and well-being of vulnerable children and adults. If the person who reported the concern or incident feels that the matter is not being dealt with by the organisation, then the matter should be referred to Care Inspectorate Wales, Social Services, or other relevant organisations. This will ensure that all information is reported and acted upon.

- If the health and social care worker has reported an incident or a concern they have seen at work (though not always), and if no action is taken by the organisation, then the health and social care worker can, under these circumstances, disclose details of the incident or wrongdoing to other parties. The incidents or their concerns must, however, be to safeguard a vulnerable person and in the public interest. This means the incident or the concern must affect others within the health and care sector – this is known as 'whistleblowing'. Details of the whistleblowing policy should be included within the staff handbook of the organisation. Staff can, and should, raise their concern about a safeguarding incident at any time without any fear of being disadvantaged within the organisation.

Legislation, regulation, and codes of conduct and practice for safeguarding and protecting children at risk

Section 5.1 of the Social Services Well-being (Wales) Act 2014 includes a definition of a 'child at risk'. The Children Act 2004 was strengthened in 2014 as a result of the **Victoria Climbié** case. Victoria Climbié died in the intensive care unit of St Mary's Hospital in Paddington in 2000, aged eight years and three months. Her death was caused by abuse and ill-treatment by her great-aunt, Marie-Therese Kouao, and her great-aunt's partner, Carl John Manning. As a result of Victoria's death, a report known as the **Laming Report** was completed in 2009 and highlighted major failings of protecting Victoria from harm and abuse. The report made 58 recommendations which were included within the Children Act 2014.

Another case illustrating a failure of safeguarding and protecting children at risk is that of **Star Hobson**, who died in September 2020 after enduring months of abuse at the hands of her mother, Frankie Smith, and her partner, Savannah Brockhill. Both were convicted in relation to her death. Star was only 16 months old when she died.

▲ Star Hobson

▲ Victoria Climbié

Activity 1

1. Research and prepare a brief summary of some examples of recent child abuse cases within Wales or the UK.

2. What kind of 'failings' come to light with these tragic child abuse cases?

The Social Services and Well-being (Wales) Act 2014 – protecting people at risk

- Promote **prevention** and **early intervention**.
- Give a **voice to each individual**, allowing the individual to have a **better control of events**.
- Promote the use of **advocates** when required.
- Provide **protection** for those identified as 'people at risk'.
- Ensures that **action** is taken in cases where abuse is suspected.
- Individuals and carers both have a **right to an assessment of need**.
- Enables the use of **Adult Protection Support Orders (APSOs)** if needed.
- **Duty to report** to relevant partners.
- Promotes the **principle of safeguarding** as fundamental.
- Local authorities have new powers to **make enquiries** if there is reasonable cause to suspect that a person is at risk.

Duty to make an enquiry

The Social Services and Well-being (Wales) Act 2014 makes it clear that when a local authority has reasonable cause to suspect that a person is at risk, then the local authority should hold an investigation and make further enquiries. The Social Services department of the local authority must respond to reports or referrals regarding any person who may be at risk of abuse and neglect. These tasks will be carried out by social workers and social services staff who work for the local authority. The key requirement and guiding principle in any investigation or enquiry is the **safety** of the individual.

Did you know?
Investigations and enquiries are two different concepts

An **investigation** involves multi-agency cooperation to gather evidence and provide learning outcomes as to whether an individual has been placed at risk of abuse or neglect or not.

An **enquiry** is a legal process describing the systematic information gathering by Social Services to determine whether any action should be taken.

Social Services and Well-being (Wales) – key volumes

The Social Services and Well-being (Wales) Act 2014 – *Working Together to Safeguard People: Volume 1 – Introduction and Overview* and *Volume 5 – Handling Individual Cases to Protect Children at Risk*, provides information about implementing the Children Act 2004 and the Social Services and Well-being (Wales) Act 2014.

The key requirements and general principles from both Volume 1 and Volume 5 focus on the following:

- That the **duty to report children and adults at risk** shall be a legal requirement for health and social care workers, relevant partners, and professionals to report any safeguarding concerns regarding individuals. The local authority also has a 'duty to investigate'.

- **A co-ordinated rights-centred approach** is needed, which includes two fundamental principles that every local authority should adopt: namely, the principles that safeguarding is everyone's responsibility, and that a person-centred approach is a paramount consideration.

- **Co-production working relations** so that each individual and their family members feel respected and informed.

- **Health and social care workers have a 'duty of confidentiality'.** However, this duty should be breached if this is in the best interests of the child or the wider public.

Activity 2

CASE STUDY – EFA

Efa is six-years old and is fed through a nasogastric (NG) feeding tube. A social networking group for Efa has been set up by her parents. Recently, a member of the public watched a video shared on Efa's social networking group. A member of the public was concerned after watching the video that her parents did not wash their hands before feeding Efa, and that her home environment appeared to be lacking in cleanliness. A complaint was made by the member of the public that Efa was at risk of harm and neglect within her home environment.

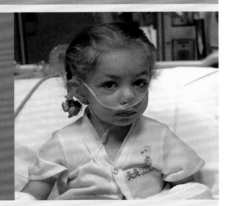

Following the complaint, Efa's parents have advised that social workers cannot speak with Efa without their consent. What are the advantages and disadvantages of Efa's parents' request?

Working Together to Safeguard People

Volume 1 – Introduction Working Together to Safeguard People
https://www.gov.wales/sites/default/files/publications/2019-05/
working-together-to-safeguard-people-volume-i-introduction-and-
overview.pdf

- Organisations that work with people should have **clear procedures** for raising concerns, and all staff should understand the procedure for making a report about the organisation or another member of staff. This is known as **whistleblowing**.

- Organisations should have **clear policies** for dealing with allegations against people in positions of trust. The statutory document gives clear guidelines on what should happen if an organisation removes an individual from working with a child, whether they are a paid worker or unpaid volunteer. Organisations must make a referral to the **Disclosure and Barring Service (DBS)**.

- Local authorities should record when a child's name is placed on the **Child Protection Register**. Local authorities should be able to demonstrate and produce a list of all the children who are on the Child Protection Register within their area (which also includes those who have been placed there by another local authority and who are considered to be at continuing risk of significant harm).

- It will be necessary to prepare a **Care and Support Plan** for persons who are at risk in order to establish and implement a care and support plan for them. In the case of a carer, a support plan only would also need to be arranged for that individual.

Volume 5 – Handling Individual Cases to Protect Children at Risk
https://www.gov.wales/sites/default/files/publications/2019-05/
working-together-to-safeguard-people-volume-5-handling-individual-
cases-to-protect-children-at-risk.pdf

Provides guidance on the process for reporting and managing risk of abuse, neglect, or harm of children. All relevant partners should be alert to the well-being needs and safety of a child, **including an unborn child**. Relevant partners should also know what and when, and to whom, they should report any concerns.

Volume 6 – Handling Individual Cases to Protect Adults at Risk
https://www.gov.wales/sites/default/files/publications/2019-06/
volume-6-handling-individual-cases-to-protect-adults-at-risk.pdf

- **Relevant Partners** should have a clear identifiable single point of contact within the local authority to ensure that they are able to report any concerns about an adult at risk. This would ensure the service is accessible and that individuals could gain support quickly and easily in reporting any concerns. It also promotes the principle that **safeguarding is everyone's business**.

- If concerns relate to the quality of care and support in a regulated setting, local authorities should **share information** with the relevant regulatory bodies.

- The local authority has a **duty to enquire** and to protect adults at risk, and to decide whether any action is needed.

- A **co-ordinated person-centred approach** is a key principle of effective safeguarding systems with a clear understanding of what is important to the individual. This approach needs to reflect the individual's wishes and ambitions.

- A **multi-agency approach** is a key requirement in safeguarding adults at risk.

- The legislation also includes **advocacy** as a key principle of this legislation, and includes a dedicated Code of Practice under Part 10 of the Act. This sets out how advocacy can provide a support framework for each individual and the requirements required by local authorities to **arrange an independent professional advocate**.

- Adults at risk must be supported and empowered, with the **right to family life** being a priority when interventions are considered.

- **Adult Protection and Support Orders** (**APSOs**) may be considered, but only in exceptional circumstances.

- **Welsh language requirements** – the process of any safeguarding enquiries must recognise the concept of the language need, and local authorities should be **proactive** in their approach; individuals at the beginning of the process should be asked which language they would prefer.

- Information must not be shared in accordance, with the **Data Protection Act** and the common law duty of confidentiality. There is, however, an exception when personal information can be lawfully shared without the consent of the person. This exception is when there is a legal requirement, or that a professional worker deems it to be in the public interest, and that the action will prevent abuse or serious harm to others.

What, when and how to report concerns for vulnerable adults, children, and young people at risk

The Social Services and Well-being (Wales) Act 2014 makes it clear that safeguarding is everyone's business, and that all individuals should be protected from abuse and neglect. Safeguarding involves not only protecting individuals who are experiencing actual abuse or neglect, but also educating those supporting people at risk to recognise the signs and dangers. It is important to remember that abuse and neglect does not need to have taken place before health and social care workers report any concerns they may have.

1   Health and social care workers must be aware of what comprises abuse and neglect. Within the statutory documents, it makes clear reference to different types of abuse and neglect, and the indicators of these types of abuse and neglect.

2   When receiving a disclosure (whether this is direct or indirect) of abuse or neglect, the team member should stay calm and not show shock. It is important that confidentiality is not promised, or that promises are made which cannot be kept. Disclosures can be direct or indirect. **Direct disclosure** is when an individual informs someone directly that they are at risk, or are being abused or neglected. **Indirect disclosure** is when a third party raises concerns regarding an individual who may be being abused or neglected. This might be because of behaviours, or indicators that an individual may be at risk.

3   Health and social care workers must take disclosures very seriously, and not make any value judgements on the accuracy of the disclosure. Health and social care workers have a duty to report and make a record of any disclosures. Health and social care workers should make a record of the interaction and disclosure as soon as possible, since this may be the first and only account available to the police or other agencies.

4   If an individual is in immediate danger, the health and social care worker should ring 999 (Emergency services) to inform them, so that the relevant agencies may be alerted.

5   Health and social care workers have a duty to report not only incidents within their work environment, but also those that take place during their daily private lives.

Safeguarding Boards

The **National Independent Safeguarding Board** was set up following the Social Services and Well-being (Wales) Act 2014 to advise the Welsh Government and to work with local safeguarding boards to protect children and adults from harm. The National Independent Safeguarding Board (NISB) aims to:

- provide support and advice to local safeguarding boards with the aim of ensuring their effectiveness. These local safeguarding boards play a crucial role in safeguarding children and adults within their local board areas. The boards' duties include protecting individuals who are experiencing, or at risk of, abuse, neglect, or other forms of harm, as well as protecting them from such risks.

- report on the adequacy and effectiveness of arrangements to safeguard children and adults across Wales. They assess and report on the adequacy and effectiveness of the arrangements in place to safeguard children and adults. By monitoring these arrangements, the National Independent Safeguarding Board contributes to improving safeguarding practices and outcomes. The National Board does provide support and advice, but it does not have a supervisory role over the local safeguarding boards.

The National Independent Safeguarding Board also make recommendations to Welsh Ministers and the Welsh Government on how safeguarding arrangements can be improved.

The six members of the National Independent Safeguarding Board work part-time and meet at least once a month, while carrying out the above duties.

Regional Safeguarding Boards were strengthened in order to establish and maintain coordinated multi-agency partnerships that would work closely together. Each local authority was required to protect adults and children with care and support needs to protect them from abuse, harm, and neglect. The Regional Safeguarding Boards were required to provide a person-centred approach with a focus on outcomes. A Regional Safeguarding Board will have Safeguarding Children's Boards and Safeguarding Adults' Boards within them.

There are six Regional Safeguarding Boards in Wales that deal with the safeguarding of children and adults at risk:

Cardiff and Vale of Glamorgan **www.cardiffandvalersb.co.uk**

Cwm Taf Morgannwg **www.cwmtafmorgannwgsafeguardingboard.co.uk**

Gwent Safeguarding **www.gwentsafeguarding.org.uk**

Mid and West Wales **cysur.wales**

North Wales **www.northwalessafeguardingboard.wales**

West Glamorgan **www.wgsb.wales**

Local Safeguarding Children Boards (LSCB) were established following Lord Laming's inquiry into the death of Victoria Climbié; the Children Act 2004 required all local authorities across England and Wales to set up a Local Safeguarding Children Board (LSCB). The task of each LSCB is to safeguard and promote the welfare of children and young people in their area. The three main objectives included:

- to identify and prevent abuse, neglect or other types of harm that affects the health and well-being of children and young people
- to be pro-active in safeguarding specific groups of vulnerable children and young people
- to safeguard and protect vulnerable children and young people from harm, abuse, neglect in their local area.

The Social Services and Well-being (Wales) Act 2014 established the National Independent Safeguarding Board to provide support and advice to these safeguarding boards to ensure that they provide an effective service. The National Independent Safeguarding Board also reviews and reports on the effectiveness of arrangements to safeguard children and adults in Wales, and makes recommendations to Welsh Ministers on how to improve the service provided.

The Social Services and Well-being (Wales) Act 2014 also established both Children's Safeguarding Boards and Adult Safeguarding Boards. In some areas, these may join into one safeguarding board. Under Part 7 of the Social Services and Well-being (Wales) Act 2014 (the 2014 Act), local authorities must establish Safeguarding Children Boards comprising representatives from local authorities, the local police body, local health board, NHS Trust, clinical commissioning groups, probation board, youth offending team and others.

The Regional Safeguarding Boards have a Safeguarding Board Lead Partner to be the lead partner for each of the Safeguarding Children Boards, and for each of the Safeguarding Adults Boards.

Safeguarding Adults Boards

The Social Services and Well-being (Wales) Act 2014 also defines an adult at risk as being anyone 18 years of age or older. The 2014 Act states that the objectives of the Safeguarding Boards are to protect adults within their areas who:

- are experiencing, or are at risk of, abuse or neglect
- have need of care and support.

Safeguarding Adults Boards (SAB) are muti-agency partnerships to promote the well-being of adults as set out under Part 7 of the Social Services and Well-being (Wales) Act 2014. The objectives of the 2014 Act were placed on protecting adults within their local area who have care and support needs who are experiencing or are at risk of abuse or neglect.

Activity 3

CASE STUDY – MEGAN AND IWAN

Megan and Iwan are in their 80s, and have lived in the same house, since they were married. Megan is unwell, and Iwan is unable to look after Megan on his own. They both speak Welsh as their first language. The Social Services and Well-being (Wales) Act 2014 has changed the way an individual's needs are assessed, and the way services are delivered.

1. Explain how the Social Services and Well-being (Wales) Act 2014 will assess Megan and Iwan's needs, and how Social Services will deliver those services, which could enable Megan and Iwan to stay in their family home.

2. One of the key principles of the Social Services and Well-being (Wales) Act 2014 is the prevention of a social care issue, and to intervene as soon as possible. Discuss how both Megan and Iwan's health and well-being could be affected by not receiving an early assessment.

Explain how an early resolution of Megan and Iwan's health and social care issues could be achieved by referring to the legislation and safeguarding procedures in Wales.

Activity 4

CASE STUDY – JAYNE

Jayne is a child who has had a difficult upbringing. Her family has a turbulent family history, with both parents arguing and abusing each other and neglecting Jayne. Her stepfather and mother often did not prepare food for her or take care of her. She was often harmed if she didn't do exactly as her stepfather or mother said. As Jayne was being neglected and abused, the social services called regularly

with the family in an effort to restore the care that Jayne needed. One of the reasons why her parents behaved irresponsibly was their regular abuse of alcohol and drugs. When Jayne was nine years old, her stepfather and mother were sent to prison for stealing money to pay for drugs, damaging property and causing serious injury to a person in a fight.

Following the imprisonment of both parents, the decision was then made by social services that Jayne would need to move to live in a foster home. The foster family were very kind and caring, but Jayne was unfamiliar with keeping their rules. Rules she didn't often agree with. Jayne often felt forced to do things she didn't want to do. This caused Jayne to be aggressive.

By the time Jayne was 11, she had started to misbehave in high school. It was all so new and unfamiliar to her. Some of the children even bullied her, as she had a slight stutter. Jayne also found it difficult to do schoolwork and to keep to the different rules. The school rules were not fair in her opinion, and she started being absent from school several times without the school's permission. She also became friends with another girl from the school, who was older than Jayne. The two would often disappear from school together to the city. Jayne's foster parents were trying to help her with her schoolwork, and show her the importance of keeping to the school rules. But this would often lead to an argument. The foster parents did not want Jayne to be friends with her older friend, who, in their opinion, was a bad influence on her, as they also thought the friend was taking drugs.

1. Examine the factors that contributed to Jayne being at risk of abuse and neglect in the past.

2. Outline the current risks of abuse and neglect that should be forwarded to social services and the multi-disciplinary team.

Activity 5

Jayne is now aged 17, and has, with the help of a multi-disciplinary team (MDT), including her social worker and a counsellor, processed the events that happened in her past and understands how they have contributed to her current situation. Jayne was assigned a female social worker because it was felt that it would benefit Jayne, and help her feel less threatened. During this time, Jayne started to use racist language. When questioned on this, Jayne informed another social worker that she had overheard support workers using similar language and she had therefore thought that this was acceptable.

Jayne has recently successfully completed an unpaid work placement, and is hoping to be accepted on a Beauty and Hairdressing course at her local further education college. Jayne is currently living in supported living accommodation. She receives support from supported living staff in learning the necessary life skills. Jayne is keen to move into social housing accommodation; however, her social worker feels that Jayne does not have the necessary skills to manage the tenancy. Jayne does not currently have any contact with her birth mother or foster family. Despite this, she has not closed the door on renewing her relationship with both her mother and her foster parents.

1. Examine how relevant legislation, codes of conduct and practice can safeguard and protect Jayne and other young people at risk.

2. Assess how health and social care practices can safeguard individuals such as Jayne.

Reading and further research

Children Act 2004
https://www.legislation.gov.uk/ukpga/2004/31/contents

Children's Commissioner for Wales
https://www.childcomwales.org.uk/about-us/

Code of Professional Practice and guidance
https://socialcare.wales/dealing-with-concerns/codes-of-practice-and-guidance

Codes of Professional Practice and Guidance
https://socialcare.wales/dealing-with-concerns/codes-of-practice-and-guidance

https://www.nmc.org.uk/standards/code/

Regulation and Inspection of Social Care (Wales) 2016
https://socialcare.wales/hub/regulation-and-inspection

Safeguarding in Wales
https://www.gov.wales/safeguarding-guidance

Social Services and Well-being (Wales) Act 2014
https://www.legislation.gov.uk/anaw/2014/4/contents

ACTIVITY ANSWERS
Activity 1

The evidence confirms that the majority of child abuse cases have occurred due to failures in safeguarding processes and procedures due to some safeguarding professionals failing to fulfil their duties in accordance with legislation, codes of practice and procedures. These failures led to children being exposed to harm, abuse, and neglect and to some children losing their lives. The main failures included:

- The **Paramountcy Principle** had not been applied. Children should be at the heart of all decisions, and any safeguarding concern should be highlighted and responded to as soon as possible. This principle also relates to *Working Together to Safeguard People: Volume 5 – Handling Individual Cases to Protect Children at Risk*, namely by adopting a child-centred approach where the rights of the child are the main focus. The best interests of the child should always be paramount. There should be a clear understanding of the child's personal wishes and outcomes and what matters to the child.

- More **consultation with the child** was required. Children should always have a choice and a degree of control regarding their life and their basic right to be heard. They should be consulted in any decision regarding their care. The **Children Act** created a **Children's Commissioner** to champion the views and interests of children.

- Deficiencies in cooperation and partnership frameworks between professionals and failures as regards adopting a multi-disciplinary approach. Failure in implementing a partnership and accountability approach and making sure that safeguarding is everyone's concern. Robust partnership arrangements between local authorities, health and social care providers and the police should always be active in promoting children's well-being.

ACTIVITY ANSWERS
Activity 2 – Efa

The advantages and disadvantages of the request for parental consent before talking to Efa:

The advantage of the request is that the social worker, under normal circumstances, needs to ask for the parent's permission to speak to a child.

The disadvantage of the request is that there is concern over the safety of the child in the family home, following the complaint raised in the social media post. There are safeguarding concerns, which may compromise their enquiries. The safety of the child is the most important factor of all, and professionals may make decisions which the parents disagree with.

If a parent refuses to give consent for a social worker to speak to the child on their own, professionals may become concerned about the child's safety and well-being. This can result in children's services becoming more involved; for example, a court order can be sought to ensure the child's safety.

When speaking with the child, social workers must observe and communicate in a manner appropriate to the child's age and understanding.

ACTIVITY ANSWERS
Activity 3 – Megan and Iwan

1. The Social Services and Well-being (Wales) Act 2014 supports Megan and Iwan to continue to live in their own home.

- Megan and Iwan are fully involved in the discussion and strategy to respond to their care and support needs.

- Social services will need to discuss with Megan and Iwan the support that they already receive, and identify where they need extra help to remain living in their own home.

- The assessment processes should progress at pace, so that Megan and Iwan should not have to wait a long time for the support they need.

- Iwan, as the carer for Megan, has also an equal right to be assessed and to receive support, in addition to the support received for Megan.

2. Prevention and early intervention are promoted by the Social Services and Well-being (Wales) Act 2014.

The positive effects on Iwan's health and well-being could include:

- Iwan's physical and mental well-being should be improved, because any issues regarding his support for Megan have beeen identified. An action plan for Iwan will be prepared to prevent negative impacts on his health, so Iwan is supported in his role as a carer.

- Iwan will be more able to support Megan if he gets the help that he needs, at the right time.

- Iwan may feel less stressed and worried by his and Megan's health and well-being knowing that appropriate support is available for both of them.

The negative effects on Iwan's health and well-being could include:

- Iwan may experience a lowered self-concept, self-esteem, and self-image of himself as a caring husband, since his role in caring for Megan may have changed.

- Iwan may feel that involving others in the care of Megan reduces the level of control that he has in supporting and caring for his wife.

- He may have enjoyed the caring and loving relationship he had with his wife, and dislike the involvement of professional health and social care workers in her care.

ACTIVITY ANSWERS
Activity 4 – Jayne

1. The factors that contributed to Jayne being at risk of abuse and neglect in the past.

These factors include:

- **Maternal neglect:** Jayne was physically abused by her mother and her stepfather. She was neglected because both of them were drug addicts and unable to provide safe care for her. Jayne was identified as a child at risk. Jayne was moved to a foster home when she was nine years old, following the imprisonment of both parents.

- **Physical abuse:** Jayne was physically abused by her parents during her time at the family home.

- **Truancy from school:** Jayne become more vulnerable to neglect and abuse due to her truancy, since Jayne was absent from the care and the safe environment that the school provided.

2. The current risks of abuse and neglect that should be forwarded to social services and the multi-disciplinary team:

- Jayne was negatively influenced by the racist language of some of her support team. She is an individual who can easily be influenced by others, and she has already shown criminal, aggressive, and negative behavioural characteristics of a vulnerable person.

- There could be concern that her foster parents will be unable to manage and support her at home, as Jayne has become a teenager, and that she has experienced the trauma of a difficult upbringing as a child and teenager.

ACTIVITY ANSWERS
Activity 5 – Jayne

1. Examine how relevant legislation, codes of conduct and practice can safeguard and protect Jayne and other young people at risk.

The command verb is 'Examine', which means that you need to show a thorough knowledge of the relevant laws and codes of conduct and practice which safeguard and protect Jayne.

The relevant legislation, codes of conduct and practice could include the Social Services and Well-being (Wales) Act 2014, the Children Act 2004, the Wales Safeguarding Procedures (2019) and the Welsh Government Safeguarding Guidance.

2. Assess how health and social care practices can safeguard individuals such as Jayne.

The command verb is 'Assess', which requires making judgements according to the value or significance of the factors.

You need to make an assessment of the health and social care safeguarding practices available to meet Jayne's needs. The assessment will need to include:

■ Providing empowerment, so that Jayne is supported and encouraged to make her own decisions and give informed consent.

■ How best to implement robust strategies to keep her safe and preventing her from being harmed. It's imperative that these strategies are put in place as soon as possible.

■ Proportionality – the team will need to put in place the least intrusive response that is appropriate to the risk presented. Jayne has not closed the door on renewing her relationship with her mother and her adoptive parents, but this arrangement would need to be organised and managed by Social Services.

■ Requirement to offer protection, support, representation, and advice on the advocacy services that are available.

■ Arrange partnership working within the local community, offering a range of services provided by the health and social care sectors, such as psychologists, counsellors, and therapy workers.

■ Ensure that the services provided include accountability checks and transparency in the safeguarding practices. All contact and plans of action need to be recorded, monitored, reviewed, and evaluated so that Jayne receives the support that reflects her desired outcomes if possible.

Jayne will be classified as an adult when she is 18, and when the support she has received as a child may not be available. At 18, Jayne is regarded as an adult who is able to make decisions by herself. However, care and support are available up to the age of 21, if the young person has been in care, or up to 25, if they've been in care and are still in education. The transition from care to independence for many young people with care experience is often challenging and difficult. Over recent years, successive campaigns across the UK have led to significant changes and the introduction of arrangements that may enable young people ready to move into independence.

If Jayne is recognised as a vulnerable adult at risk, she could receive an Adult Protection and Support Order (APSO). An Adult Protection and Support Order is a legal mechanism used to enable an authorised officer to speak, in private, to an adult suspected of being at risk of abuse or neglect, to establish whether the adult can make decisions freely, to assess whether the person is an adult at risk, and to establish if any action should be taken. In the majority of instances, the person has to consent to the local authority applying for an order. The order can be applied for in magistrates' courts. An APSO, however, is only available in exceptional circumstances.

5.4: Practices and approaches in securing the rights of individuals at risk in health and social care settings

*The rights of adults and children at risk of neglect and abuse need to be protected. In order to achieve this, a number of practices and approaches must be adopted. A useful acronym to **remember** the important **practices** is '**CARS'**, and a useful acronym to **remember the approaches** is '**APPEALS'**.*

Practices to be implemented

Health and Social Care workers need to adopt and implement the following best practices to safeguard vulnerable children, young people, and adults. Practices which can safeguard vulnerable children, young people, and adults at risk of abuse, harm or neglect can be summarised by the acronym CARS.

Codes of practice and legislation must be in place and followed (and the consequences if not): clear rules to follow with legal consequences if not followed.

Allowing individuals to feel that they have a voice, a choice and that they have some control for their lives. Adopting this practice should make every individual feel they are the focal point for the care and the service provided.

Rapport – creating a good relationship with individuals will foster good interaction and robust relationships.

Safe environment – individuals feel more confident and able to communicate easily within a safe environment.

Approaches to be implemented

Health and Social Care workers need to adopt and implement the following approaches to safeguard vulnerable children, young people, and adults. Approaches which can safeguard vulnerable children, young people, and adults can be summarised by the acronym APPEALS.

Active participation – by encouraging each individual to take part in the activities and build relationships with others on a day-to-day basis in order to allow each individual to live as independently as possible. Active participation regards each individual as an active partner in their own care or support.

Principles of care are being applied – the way health and social workers should behave towards individuals in their care to provide their right of choice, dignity, and respect.

Personalised care – focusing on a person-centred approach to provide an individual with the care and support needed to achieve the best outcomes by identifying the most important resources and activities.

Empowerment – encouraging an individual to be more active in their health and decision-making regarding care and support. A definition of empowerment in health and social care is a process that gives people more control over the decisions and actions that impact their lives. A conscious effort should be made by health and social care workers to give service users a choice, such as the gender of their carer, preferences surrounding their daily routine and their overall goals and wishes. Care workers should think about ways to ensure people have real choices that they can make, and act on the things that are important to them.

Advocacy – being offered when appropriate to inform individuals about their rights and supporting them to express their views, ensuring that their voice is heard.

Legislation – ensuring that the rights of individuals are upheld.

Safeguarding training and information awareness on safeguarding for health and social care workers and anyone who may see evidence or receive disclosures to protect individuals in the wider community. The main consideration is how best to safeguard the individuals within their communities,` whatever the vulnerability context (for example, a disclosure from a taxi driver who is taking a young adult who has Additional Special Needs to college).

Safeguarding training | Social Care Wales

Governance

Governance is also an approach that safeguards individuals at risk. This is a process by which the health and social care sector provides good quality service delivery and promotes positive outcomes for individuals who use the service. This governance is provided in Wales by **Care Inspectorate Wales** (which inspects and monitors social care) and **Healthcare Inspectorate Wales** (which monitors healthcare).

 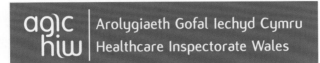

Legislation and Codes of Practices that can safeguard individuals

There are legislation requirements and good practice guidelines that health and social care workers should follow to protect individuals from harm, abuse, and neglect. These include ensuring that **legislation** and **codes of practice** are followed that will allow individuals to have a voice, an ability to make choices and to have a degree of control in their lives. It's important that health and social care workers develop a good **rapport** with each individual within a safe environment if this is to be achieved.

When implemented, codes of practice reduce the risk of harm by:

✔ protecting the rights of individuals, such as rights to live safely and free from danger, harm, neglect, or abuse.

✔ promoting the interests of each individual.

✔ promoting the independence of each individual.

✔ empowering individuals by encouraging them to make their own decisions and provide informed consent.

✔ ensuring health and social care workers are accountable. Staff need to have a sound knowledge and understanding of legislation, good practice, approaches, and governance in order to effectively support individuals in reaching their desired outcomes.

✔ supporting the well-being of individuals at risk.

- The practices as stated in the codes of practice set the **standards** that an individual at risk should expect from any health and social care workers who are supporting them achieve their desired outcomes.

- The concept of **well-being** is wide ranging, but it does include being protected from abuse and neglect.

- An **assessment of need** takes place to support an individual's well-being when in need of care and support. Sometimes, an individual's carer may also be assessed for their needs at the same time. During the assessment, an individual or carer can be signposted to other services that can help, and prevent them from needing further support.

If the needs of the individual at risk or their carer cannot be met by preventative services, then a care and support plan should be developed.

The consequences of legislation and codes of practices not being followed include the following:

- An individual could be at a greater risk of harm, neglect, or abuse.

- Disciplinary action being taken against a health and social care worker for not following the relevant legislation or codes of practice.

- Health and social workers could be removed from the register of their profession.

- A greater risk is that a health or social care worker could be injured or harmed.

- The health and social care setting or the service provider can be prosecuted under the law.

Activity 1

CASE STUDY – MENNA

Menna has cognitive impairments, and the discharge team are in the process of working with Menna and her family to arrange her living arrangements in the future. The discharge team is a multi-disciplinary team of professionals who are responsible for Menna's care and well-being. Menna has made it clear that she does not want to move into a residential care home.

Examine in detail the arguments for and against moving Menna to a residential care home.

Social Services and Well-being (Wales) Act 2014

The Social Services and Well-being (Wales) Act 2014 emphasises that individuals should have a voice, a choice and control regarding their care and support. Individuals need to feel like an equal partner in their care and support with their health and social care team. Effective safeguarding systems are those which promote a person-centred approach, as indicated by the statutory documents **Working Together to Safeguard People Volume 5** and **Volume 6**. A person-centred approach focuses on having a clear understanding of the desired **personal outcomes** that the individual at risk wishes to achieve, and what matters to that individual.

> It is important that the rights of an individual are at the core of all safeguarding practices and that the best interests of every individual are respected and acted upon by the health and social care worker. Good practice will be achieved successfully by health and care workers who can effectively connect with individuals at risk so that they feel they have a voice, a choice, and an ability to be part of the process during their care and support.

This may be achieved by:

- making sure that all communication with the individual is clear in the language and format of their choice
- advocacy services being available so that each individual has an opportunity to air their views effectively
- ensuring that the contributions of family members, friends and community members are heard and encouraged, when appropriate
- arranging 'what matters' conversations with all individuals
- explaining the rights and entitlements to every individual at risk.

Activity 2

CASE STUDY – GINA

Gina is 85 years old. She has been living in her own flat with help and support with daily living tasks from her son Anthony. Anthony has been struggling to cope with the increasing demands of caring for his mother, as he has a family of his own, but Gina is keen to stay in her family home and not move to alternative accommodation. Anthony has raised the issue of his mother moving to live in a residential care home.

Explain in detail how Gina's health and social care workers can best respond to the issue within the context of the legislation and codes of practice. Legislation and codes of practice that state that health and social care workers must allow Gina and Anthony to have a voice, a choice and control during the process of ensuring the well-being of Gina as a vulnerable person.

Rapport with individuals at risk

It's important to talk and develop a good rapport with individuals at risk. This enables **individuals to feel comfortable**; as a result, they are more likely to speak openly and feel more confident while being supported with their care and support needs. Health and social care workers should provide person-centred care by identifying what is most important to the individual, enabling the individual to feel like an **equal partner** and as a result, feel **valued**. If health and social care workers are consistent in their approach, this will enable individuals to feel a sense of **security** and **stability**, which supports the development of a positive relationship.

Rapport involves nurturing a **close and harmonious relationship** in which individuals are valued and as a result, provides an opportunity to speak more freely. It's important that this is established and nurtured at the beginning of the relationship.

Ways in which health and social care workers can develop a rapport with individuals at risk include:

- ✔ Listening to the individual.
- ✔ Providing person-centred care.
- ✔ Being fair and consistent.
- ✔ Maintaining confidentiality of information.
- ✔ Finding more about an individual's history, focusing on their strengths.
- ✔ Being open and transparent.

Health and social care workers would provide person-centred care by identifying what is most important to the individual so that the individual feels like an equal partner and as a result, they feel valued. If health and social care workers are consistent in their approach, this will enable individuals to feel a sense of security and stability, which supports the development of a positive relationship.

Maintaining confidentiality of information

Maintaining **confidentiality of information** is really important when working with individuals at risk. It's crucial that an individual has the confidence to feel that what they say will be in confidence, and therefore that their right to a 'private life' is safeguarded.

Confidentiality cannot always be achieved – it can be broken if there is a threat to a child or an adult, or to others.

Being open and transparent with individuals at risk improves the rapport. For example, if health and social care workers have misunderstood or made an error, it's really important to be honest with the individual. Maintaining confidentiality is known as **duty of candour**. Being open and honest will build a bond of trust between the individual at risk and the health and social care worker.

Preparing a safe environment

Providing a safe environment is important when health and social care workers are caring and supporting individuals at risk. The **Health and Safety at Work Act 1974** makes it clear that employers, employees and the self-employed must work in a safe way. Health and social care workers are responsible for taking reasonable care of themselves and others by following policies and procedures and not acting in a way which may cause harm to individuals who require different types of care and support. It is crucial that health and social care workers provide a safe environment. An important consideration for health and social care workers is that they must provide a safe environment for carrying out their duties or activities. They must have sufficient training and have the ability and competence to perform their duties well. They must not perform any duties or activities that they have not be trained for or are not deemed competent to perform.

Approaches that can safeguard individuals

Active participation

Active participation is a way of working that supports an individual's right to participate in everyday activities and relationships as independently as possible. Individuals are regarded as active and practising partners in their own care, rather than passive recipients. Active participation applies to adults and children at risk at any stage of their lives. This could also include parents/carers who can support their active participation.

Legislation, Standards and Codes of Conduct are important to ensure that an individual's rights are upheld:

- The Human Rights Act 1998.

- The Social Services and Well-being (Wales) Act 2014, including other relevant legislation as stated within the statutory documents.

- National standards set as NHS Health and Social Care Standards.

- The health and social care codes of professional practice and codes of conduct.

How can health and social care workers create a safe environment for service users?

- A requirement to have a detailed understanding of the codes or practice, including specific requirements regarding safeguarding and control of harmful substances.

- Workers must wear protective clothing when interacting with service users – this could be Personal Protective Equipment (PPE), such as gloves, face shields or goggles.

- Workers must ensure the security of gates and doors, so service users can be kept safe.

- Risk assessment in the health and social care sector is the systematic identification, evaluation and management of potential risks and hazards that may affect patients, clients, healthcare providers and organisations. The health and social care organisations must provide guidance and provide adequate training for workers. Risk assessments by organisations and staff is the mechanism used to identify potential hazards and to analyse what could happen if an incident or an accident occurs in the setting, and how can the risk be speedily resolved. This risk assessment process reduces the likelihood of injury or illness and creates a safer living environment for the service user.

- Workers need to be aware of the danger of revealing any unauthorised disclosures about service users. It's very important that private and confidential information is not shared with others.

- Store harmful and dangerous substances (including medication) in secure locations within the setting so that service users are not at risk.

- Workers must attend multi-disciplinary team meetings to enable health and social care professionals to share their knowledge and expertise to provide the best care and support for the service user.

- Workers must report any concerns they have about individuals who are experiencing, or who are at risk of, abuse or neglect. Safeguarding is everyone's responsibility.

- Health and social care workers must attend the training sessions provided by the organisation to ensure that staff who are required to use medical or specialised equipment fully understand the procedures.

- Health and social care settings promote a duty of care and a duty of candour (being open and honest) so that service users are aware and informed about their treatment and care plans.

Principles of care

Principles of care underpin health and social care. These principles describe the way health and social care workers should behave towards individuals who they care for and support, and this ensures individuals' rights to a choice, dignity, and respect.

Principles of care	How can the principles of care be applied to enable total quality health and social care?
Promoting effective communication and good relationships	■ Ensuring communication is clear and in the language (including Welsh as an Active Offer) and format of choice. ■ "What matters to me". ■ Keeping clear and accurate records in accordance with legislation. ■ Avoid making promises that cannot be kept, e.g. stating that information will not be shared, even when it's known that the promise cannot be kept. ■ Encourage individuals to be 'active participants.' ■ Being consistent in approach.
Promoting equality and diversity – including anti-discriminatory practice (as set out in policies/codes of practice)	■ Respecting individuals with unique backgrounds and preferences. ■ Avoiding making assumptions. ■ Challenging and reporting discrimination, harassment and hate crime. ■ Offering choices of food and drink that take personal beliefs and values and religious and cultural needs into account. ■ Supporting individuals to make a connection with a community that shares their beliefs.
Promoting individual rights and beliefs	■ Embedding legislation into practice. ■ Empowering individuals. ■ Using minimum restraint in areas of practice. Some settings that care for and support individuals with mental health disorders may have to restrain service users in order to keep them from injuring themselves or others. ■ Making sure that individuals have the support to make comments, to complain or express concerns. ■ Plan for advocacy services.
Maintaining confidentiality of information	■ It's not appropriate for health and social care workers to share service user information in public spaces, such as on a public corridor. ■ Use locked cabinets and use secure emails with password-protected documents. ■ Information should only be shared on a 'need-to-know' basis.
Providing individualised care	■ Holistic approaches – responding on the basis that each individual is unique, and meeting their physical, intellectual, emotional, and social needs. ■ Empowering individuals to live as independently as possible by providing support systems. ■ Ensuring individual personal outcomes are at the centre of their care and support needs.
Promoting safety	■ Supporting individuals to recognise potential safeguarding issues and how to report them. ■ Supporting individuals to raise any concerns. ■ Stepping back from any situation where the practitioner is unsure of how best to proceed, e.g. using specialist equipment or administering medication. ■ Reflecting on errors made and learning from the experience for future practice.

Activity 2

Prepare a simple grid diagram to identify the different principles of care that need to be supported in the following **situations:**

Situation	Principle of care
1. The GP surgery has an equal opportunity policy.	
2. The GP carries out appointments in a private room.	
3. Individuals are given prescriptions according to their condition.	
4. Individuals are asked if they prefer tablets or liquid medicine.	

Activity 3

CASE STUDY – MR FERNANDO

Mr Fernando has been admitted to his local hospital with a heart condition and is awaiting surgery. He is a practising Muslim, and he has been provided with a room to pray. In addition, Mr Fernando has a basic understanding of English but he is not fluent, so he has been provided with an interpreter. Mr Fernando requires a substantial amount of care, and was recently given a bed bath by a female nurse. The nurse did not offer Mr Fernando an opportunity not to have a bed bath, and the nurse did not draw the curtains around his bed.

The nurse then left Mr Fernando half-dressed while she responded to another patient on the same ward who had pressed their emergency bleeper. When the nurse returned, she did not speak to Mr Fernando, who seemed stressed. He was extremely upset and was also shivering. Mr Fernando had also overheard and had understood enough English to realise that a nurse was talking about his condition to a group of volunteers who support other patients on the ward.

Explain two ways in which the nurse has not provided quality care for Mr Fernando, and explain how this could affect his health and well-being.

Outline and explain how the hospital and the nurse could apply a range of principles of care and core values to provide high-quality person-centred care to Mr Fernando.

Personalised care

Personalised care (person-centred care and child-centred care) is a key concept which puts the emphasis on the individual who is accessing care and support services. Any care and support being offered to individuals should be tailored for the individual at risk, as they are at the heart of any decision-making. Personalised care is one of the key principles which is highlighted in the statutory documents, namely *Working Together to Safeguard People – Volume 5/6*. Individuals at risk should be made to feel like equal partners. Health and social care workers should identify the most important outcomes for an individual to achieve a good life and make sure that the care and support they get ensures that their desired outcomes can be achieved.

Personalised care can be implemented by health and social care workers in the following ways:

- Using a **proactive** approach to focus on what matters to the individual and what is meaningful to the individual. This enables the individual at risk to create or control a situation by causing something to happen, rather than responding to it after it has happened.

- **Supporting individuals** to achieve personal outcomes, considering the concept of well-being as noted in the Social Services and Well-being (Wales) Act 2014.

- **Respecting views and feelings** – what individuals want to achieve and what their rights are.

- Supporting individuals at risk by recognising and using their **strengths** and **abilities**.

- **Co-producing** solutions **as equal partners** and encouraging **active participation.**

Empowerment

Empowerment encourages individuals to be more active in their health and decision-making regarding their care and support. Empowerment also means effectively communicating and giving individuals information and support. In this way, they can make informed decisions and choices about their lives so that they can live as independently as possible.

There are a number of ways in which individuals at risk can be empowered:

- Putting individuals at the heart of the service provision.
- The individual's desired personal outcomes to be at the centre of their care and support strategy.
- Promote individual dignity.
- Enable individuals to express their needs and preferences.
- Enable individuals to have a voice and to make their own choices and have control over decisions, whenever possible.

Advocacy

Advocacy means speaking on behalf of someone else, to represent their interests. It is a very important approach when safeguarding individuals at risk. An advocate can enable individuals to challenge any inaccurate information and to voice any concerns they may have regarding their care and support and their well-being. Health and social care services should always consider **self-advocacy** first. This is where individuals stand up for their own rights, but if this is not possible, then advocacy services should be offered. Advocacy services must be offered if a service user has difficulty understanding, retaining, and weighing up significant information and/or communicating their views, wishes, feelings and beliefs.

Different forms of advocacies

- **Formal advocacy**
  Some broader professional roles have an element of advocacy within them. The professional can support the individual to express their views and wishes while separately expressing their own professional views or judgements.

- **Informal advocacy**
  An individual may seek advocacy support from someone they know on an informal basis. This type of advocacy forms part of a broader emotional relationship where the advocate may have their own strong feelings about what's best for the individual.

- **Professional/independent advocacy**
  An individual may be able to access an advocate whose job is to provide them with independent support to get their voice heard, regardless of their own views or opinions of the situation.

- **Peer advocacy**
  An individual might look for advocacy support from someone who understands their situation because they've been there, or are in similar circumstances to themselves.

An advocate's role is wide-ranging to represent all individuals at risk who may need **care and support**:

- Hearing their story – clarifying the issue.
- Establishing what their preferred outcome is.
- Helping them to decide what they want, including all potential outcomes.
- Helping them access accurate information.
- Helping them explore options, including processes involved in each.
- Helping them to tell others what they want.

- Advocate advises the individual on what options they think they should choose.
- Advocate discusses individual with social worker by means of de-brief.

Legislation and codes of practice – ensuring that individual rights are upheld

Legislation and codes of practice ensure that individual rights are upheld. A rights-based approach ensures that health and social care services put individuals at risk at the centre of planning and delivering services. This ensures that individual rights are upheld as stated in **the Social Service and Well-being (Wales) Act 2014**.

Working Together to Safeguard People Volume 1 / Volume 5 / Volume 6 also considers other relevant legislation, such as:

- Domestic abuse (Violence against Women, Domestic Abuse and Sexual Violence (Wales) Act 2015
- The Prohibition of Female Circumcision Act 1985
- Modern Slavery Act 2015
- Human Rights Act 1998
- The United Nations Principles for Older Persons 1991
- Mental Capacity Act 2005
- Welsh Language Act 1993
- Data Protection Act 2018 includes the UK's implementation of the EU's General Data Protection Regulation (GDPR)

Different approaches that health and social care workers can use to support the rights of individual service users:

1. Active participation: supporting independence and participation in the activities and relationships of everyday life.
2. Advocacy: informing individuals about their rights and helping them to express their views so that their voice is heard.
3. Empowerment: encouraging individuals to be more active in their decision-making.
4. Demonstrating the principles of care in their everyday work.
5. Following legislation through policies and procedures to ensure that individuals' rights are upheld.
6. Personalised care: making sure that the care and support provided ensures their personal outcomes are achieved.

CASE STUDY – SATBIR ARORA

This is Satbir Arora; he has been praised for safeguarding a girl from significant abuse and harm. Satbir is a taxi driver who established that a girl was being groomed. Satbir had spoken to the girl's potential abuser over the phone and recorded their conversations, which was later used as evidence. Satbir informed a police officer of the girl's immediate danger and, as a result, the girl was protected from further abuse or harm being caused. This case reinforces the need for information awareness and training on safeguarding for health and social care workers and other people who may see evidence or get **disclosures**. Some individuals at risk cannot drive, and therefore rely on public transport to get to places. This reinforces the need for safeguarding training for public transport workers.

Why is safeguarding training important?

- Health and social care workers are kept up to date with legislation and codes of practice.

- Staff will be made aware of the 'whistleblowing' guidelines (which can be an opportunity to raise concerns about poor practice in the health and social care sector).

- Strengthen person-centred care.

- Lessons can be learned from formal reviews of individuals who have been abused or neglected.

- Aids confidence in spotting safeguarding concerns, and how and what to report.

Governance – monitoring and inspection of health and social care services

There are two inspectorates for monitoring and inspecting health and social care services in Wales. **Care Inspectorate Wales** focuses on social care and social services, whereas **Healthcare Inspectorate Wales** focuses on health care and health services.

Care Inspectorate Wales regulates and inspects the following services:

- Adult services: care homes for adults, domiciliary support services, adult placement services and residential family centre services.

- Children's services: care homes for children, fostering services, adoption services, advocacy services and accommodation services.

- Children and play services: childminders, crèches, full day care, sessional day care, out-of-school care and open-access play provision.

- Local authority fostering and adoption services.

- Boarding schools.

- Residential special schools (boarding arrangements under 295 days).

- Further education colleges with residential accommodation for students under 18.

Healthcare Inspectorate Wales is the independent inspectorate and regulator for healthcare in Wales. It inspects NHS services and regulate independent healthcare providers against a range of standards, policies, guidance, and regulations to identify best practice and to highlight areas requiring improvement.

Its role is to encourage improvement in healthcare by doing the right job at the right time in the right place, ensuring that communication is effective and making a difference to individual lives. Its role also includes the necessity to act when standards are not being met. Healthcare Inspectorate Wales can take immediate action if the safety and quality of healthcare does not meet the required standards, and inform individuals and the public about the standards of healthcare in Wales.

Inspections by Healthcare Inspectorate Wales to ensure individuals receive high-quality care:

- Announced or unannounced inspections of healthcare settings.

- Interviews with a range of individuals who use the service.

- Able to take urgent action if there are immediate concerns.

- In-depth single ward inspections, a thorough and detailed review of one hospital ward.

- Multi-ward inspections – a number of wards and departments within one hospital site.

- Staff interviews.

- Multi-hospital inspections – visiting a number of healthcare settings within the same Health Board to assess the governance and delivery of the service within the Health Board.

Preparation for the N.E.A. tasks

Please read the two responses and the feedback provided by the examiner. The second response is a good response, providing clear and detailed references to health and social care practices required to safeguard individuals.

Identify and explain how national inspection services safeguard individuals in Wales.

Candidate 1 – Response

In Wales there is the healthcare inspectorate Wales and the care and social services inspectorate Wales. They have clear roles in safeguarding individuals. The healthcare inspectorate's role is to inspect NHS and independent healthcare providers in Wales and can close down services. If healthcare inspectorate Wales did not exist then this could lead to individuals being put at risk. In conclusion, it is clear that if healthcare inspectorate Wales and care and social services inspectorate Wales did not exist than health and social care services could continue to operate even if they delivered harmful care.

Candidate 2 – Response

Organisations that inspect health and social care services in Wales are known as Care Inspectorate Wales (CIW) and Healthcare inspectorate Wales (HIW). The first key role of the inspectorate system is to ensure individuals are treated with respect and dignity, this is key in safeguarding individuals as individuals may be at risk, so inspections focus on these situations and how well these individuals are treated and take action if needed to protect from harm and abuse. If there were no inspections, these individuals may not feel safe and as a result may not be able to access the service, so the outcomes will not be achieved.

A second key role is protecting individuals from harm and abuse. This is done by taking immediate action if healthcare providers do not meet the standards. Actions could be placed upon the provider, or the provider could even be closed down. If this was not in place, individuals at risk may be at risk or may experience further abuse or neglect.

A third key role is ensuring individuals have a voice, choice, and control in their care. This is done by ensuring that health and social care providers are meeting an individual's human rights, such as the right to have choice in their care. Inspectors can find out if individuals know about their right to complain about services. If individuals are not aware of this, they may continue to suffer and as a result their outcomes may not be met.

In conclusion, it is clear that without inspections in Wales, individuals who are at risk may not be kept safe, individuals could be harmed and even result in death and individuals' desired outcomes would not be met.

Response 1 – Feedback by the Examiner

Firstly, it is important to draw attention to the inaccurate comment over 'the care and social services inspectorate in Wales'. Even though learners are not marked down for inaccurate comments, candidates need to be aware that the inspectorate system for social care in Wales is now called – 'Care Inspectorate Wales'. This is also identified in the 5.4 section of the specification. Learners should proofread their work; there was a typing error: 'Wales' should include a capital letter.

The response showed some knowledge and understanding of the role of the inspectorate system in Wales and the consequence of not having an inspectorate system in place. It was good to see that the candidate attempted to reach a conclusion – this is good practice when attempting Assessment Objective 3 questions requiring an assessment.

Response 2 – Feedback by the Examiner

This was a more detailed response than Response 1, since it provided some clear assessment, and included reasoned judgements demonstrating good knowledge and understanding of the role of the inspectorate system. The response included the three key roles of the inspectorate system in safeguarding individuals, namely: 1) ensuring individuals are treated with dignity and respect; 2) protecting individuals from harm by taking immediate action; 3) making sure that individuals have a voice in their care.

The response also gave clear examples of how inspections were conducted and the consequences that would occur if an inspectorate system were not in place.

Reading and further research

Community Care Live 24 – Strengths-based practice in action
www.communitycare.co.uk/2019/05/24/171282

Care Inspectorate Wales
www.careinspectorate.wales

Healthcare Inspectorate Wales
https://hiw.org.uk/

Healthcare Inspectorate Wales monitoring NHS services
https://hiw.org.uk/inspect-healthcare

ACTIVITY ANSWERS
Activity 1 – Menna

The advantages of moving Menna into a care home follow the guidance provided by the Multi-Disciplinary Team (MDT) professionals, who have current and detailed knowledge about her health and well-being. The priority of the team is to keep Menna, an adult at risk, safe. The team have been involved and worked with Menna's family for a long time and are therefore able to represent her as her advocate to speak on her behalf.

The disadvantages of moving Menna into a care home is that she may protest and believe she has been moved to the home against her wishes. This could cause distress to Menna, which could have a negative effect on her health and well-being. Menna could feel that she has lost her independence and become so distressed that she wants to return to her own home. She may feel that her voice and her choice of wishing to remain in her home were not listened to by the team.

During the initial discussions with Menna, the team need to openly discuss the options and find a solution that fully considers the well-being of Menna and the obligations of the team to keep her safe.

ACTIVITY ANSWERS
Activity 2 – The Principles of Care

1. The GP surgery has an equal opportunity policy which promotes equality and diversity, promoting anti-discriminatory practices.

2. Providing a private room will offer confidentiality of information to the patient or client.

3. Prescribing according to need means that individualised care has been provided.

4. Patients were asked if they preferred to have either a tablet or a medicine dose. A choice was therefore given, so that the patient has the right of choice, which could make an individual feel more empowered.

ACTIVITY ANSWERS
Activity 3 – Mr Fernando

1. Explain two ways in which the nurse has not provided quality care for Mr Fernando, and explain how this could affect his health and well-being.

- The nurse has not maintained confidentiality. The nurse has shared information about Mr Fernando's condition to individuals who do not need to have that information. Nurses should only share information about Mr Fernando on a 'need-to-know' basis. Sharing his information with individuals who do not need to know may result in Mr Fernando not trusting the nurse and not disclosing any health issues to the nurse in the future.

- The nurse has not provided appropriate principles of care; the nurse did not promote individual rights and did not provide individualised care, since Mr Fernando did not want a bed bath. Also, the nurse had not provided Mr Fernando with his right to dignity: he was left undressed and seen by others on the ward, and his wishes were not respected. Mr Fernando could have reduced self-concept (the image we have of ourselves) because he does not feel valued, leading to a decline in self-esteem.

2. Outline and explain how the hospital and the nurse could apply a range of principles of care and core values to provide high-quality person-centred care to Mr Fernando.

The range of principles of care and core values could include:

- Promoting effective communication and relationships because the nurse did not communicate effectively with Mr Fernando.

- Promoting and supporting equality by offering individuals the right to choose. However, no choice was given regarding having a bed bath, or perhaps having a bath by a male nurse instead of a female nurse.

- Promoting safety on the ward. Mr Fernando was left partially clothed, upset, and shivering, so his physical and mental health and well-being could be negatively affected.

5.5: The ways in which individual health and social care workers and the services they provide can promote inclusion

It's important to consider the range of health and care workers who look after people's health and social care. These workers are all responsible for promoting the inclusion of those under their care. The healthcare sector offers a broad range of roles that care for the health and social care of people who need the best care.

It is also important to consider how different individuals can contribute to establishing and promoting inclusion within their settings.

The main roles of different health and social care worker staff, and how they can promote inclusion at work, are summarised below.

Health care workers	Social care workers
Nurse: nurses plan and provide medical and nursing care to patients in hospital, at home or in other settings. They focus on the care of individuals, families, and communities within an inclusive framework.	**Home care worker**: provides essential support to individuals in their own homes, helping clients to be independent and able to live their daily lives. **Adult care home worker**: provides care and support to individuals in a care home setting. **Social care worker**: provides support for people who need specialist care. Social care workers help to protect and promote people's well-being and safety. Social care workers work with individuals, families within their communities at their homes or in residential settings. Social care workers support people with their non-medical needs. They help vulnerable people to manage their daily activities and to live as independently as possible while adopting an inclusive approach.
Psychologist/Counsellor: they focus on how people think, feel, and behave, and the impact this has on them and their relationships with others.	**Nursing care provided by registered nurse:** focuses on individuals living with disabilities, immobility, and long-term medical conditions.
Psychiatrist: a trained doctor who diagnoses and treats patients with mental health issues or disorders.	**Social worker**: liaises with individuals and families to review needs and make support plans, helping clients to develop and maintain independent living skills, keeping them safe and protecting them when necessary. They work closely with communities, health professionals and other agencies.
Allied health professional: these include a wide range of professional workers – for example, an orthoptist (for eyes) and podiatrist (for feet).	**Community and outreach worker**: engages with clients within 'hard-to-reach' communities, e.g. teenagers, substance abusers and homeless people.
Speech and language therapist: they support and care for children and adults who have difficulties with speaking and communication issues, eating, drinking, and swallowing.	**Domiciliary care manager**: responsible for managing the delivery of care and support services, in line with legislative requirements and in accordance with the available funding.
Physiotherapist (also an allied health professional): helps people affected by injury, illness or disability through movement and exercise, manual therapy, education, and advice. They maintain health for people of all ages, helping patients to manage pain and prevent disease.	**Adult care home manager**: provides information, advice and support to residents, families, and staff. They manage care homes, but also help residents to access local services and provide overall quality care, according to the funding available.

➜

Dietician: an expert in nutrition and diet who promotes health, prevents disease, and encourages positive dietary choices for both healthy and people with illness.	**Advocate**: advocates are trained to support individuals to express their views and wishes, and to represent their rights.
Occupational therapist: specialises in occupational therapy using a holistic approach to promote an individual's ability to fulfil their daily routines and roles, e.g. getting dressed.	
Midwife: provides care and support for women and their families before and after the baby's birth.	

As health and social care workers progress throughout their specific roles, it is also important for them to build on existing good practice. They could also reflect on what they do. **Reflection** includes thinking carefully about something in an open-minded way which could lead to the worker becoming more self-aware and able to practise a more effective and inclusive care service. For example, if the worker lacks experience in helping visually impaired individuals to meet their desired outcomes, then reflection could lead to changing their approach or undertaking further research, and perhaps getting help from other health and social care workers to build on **good practice**.

Delivering inclusion within the work setting will involve having detailed knowledge of structured standards, protocols, policies, and guidelines. Policies are a set of guidelines that set out the organisation's plans, values, and philosophy for handling specific issues, while procedures are documents that set out in detail how a specific issue should be approached and dealt with, or how specific tasks should be carried out. These should be included during the initial induction course and in follow-up training sessions. The organisation will have in place agreed ways of working that the organisation expects health and care workers to follow. These will often include reference to a line manager and relevant documents in the form of policies and procedures.

Agreed ways of working in health and social care refer to the structured standards, protocols, policies, and guidelines that professionals in these sectors adhere to in order to ensure they provide high-quality, consistent, and safe care. Agreed ways of working may also be included within an individual's plan or within their job description. Agreed ways of working also set out ways of supporting individuals who need care and support as specified in their care plan, and other policies and procedures such as moving and handling, health and safety and safeguarding policies/procedures. Health and social care workers have roles and responsibilities set out in their contract of employment.

Key terms

Discrimination: treating a person or a group of people differently from other people because of their language, race, gender, religion, disability, and sexual orientation, for example.

Diversity: the range of differences within society, including, for example, different genders and ethnicity, sexual orientation, religion, linguistic or cultural differences, social differences, abilities, and disabilities.

Equality: treating an individual fairly and responding to an individual's needs – not just treating individuals in the same way. The state of being equal in aspects such as rights, opportunities, and status.

Harassment: aggressive pressure or intimidation.

Inclusion: children and adults at risk are included and involved in their care and support. The term 'inclusion' is linked closely both to equality and diversity. Inclusion, equality, and diversity are interlinked so that all individuals are treated fairly and with respect.

Policies: written documents setting out an organisation's approach to a particular issue.

Procedures: documents that set out in detail how a particular issue should be dealt with or how specific tasks should be carried out. Normally during a health and social care worker's induction, they would be given the policies and procedures which they agree to implement and follow.

Whistleblowing: when a worker passes on information about 'wrongdoing'; they make a disclosure about something they have seen or has happened in their workplace.

Discrimination of any kind can be detrimental to an individual's well-being. It can also be an obstacle to the individual achieving the results that the individual desires. Health and social care workers should avoid discrimination because of the adverse effects it has on individuals. The concept of discrimination is broad, and it is important that all health and social care workers avoid all forms of discrimination. It is vitally important that all health and social care workers do not show prejudice of any kind. It is therefore important that you do not 'speak your opinion' about a certain group or other individuals, thus showing prejudice. For example, if a social worker were reluctant to support an individual who has a religious belief because the worker does not agree with that belief, then that could lead to a lack of care based on prejudice. Discriminatory practice can lead to the provision of inadequate care – for example, by not meeting an individual's basic needs, such as not assisting a disabled individual to go to the toilet when necessary. Discriminatory practice can also include all different forms of abuse and neglect.

Health and social care workers need to be able create an environment which promotes inclusion and ensures that all individuals are involved in their care and support, and that they feel 'valued'. Inclusion can also mean **social inclusion**, which means providing opportunities for individuals to be involved and fully participate in their wider communities, so they feel included, and that they have a role and are part of society. This may be through accessing public transport, socialising with friends, accessing a course at a local college, and participating in a local cultural event. A key part of the Social Services and Well-being (Wales) Act 2014 is enabling individuals to achieve independence, and for individuals to be supported to improve their well-being. Health and social care services should promote the well-being of individuals by ensuring that their services offer equality of opportunity.

Health and social care workers can ensure equality of opportunity in the services they provide to promote inclusion by:

- Identifying and removing barriers to access and participation
- Enabling individuals to use the full range of services and facilities
- Valuing and supporting individuals using the services.

Ways in which individual workers and the services they provide can promote inclusion

*You Should Know: a useful acronym to remember how health and social care workers promote inclusion is **PADDLERS**. An acronym to remember the services they provide is **WEED**.*

Ways in which health and social care workers provide and promote inclusion

Principles of care being demonstrated.

Agreed ways of working being demonstrated and followed.

Discrimination by association avoided.

Discrimination by perception avoided.

Listening to individuals so they have a voice.

Equity of access and equal opportunities.

Reasonable adjustments.

Supporting diversity by working in non-judgemental ways.

Health and Social Care Workers – providing inclusion

Whistleblowing – when appropriate.

Effective communication – ensuring that all contact and communication is clear, using the language and format of the person's choice.

Ensure that no harassment is taking place.

Dignity and respect are provided at all times.

It is also important that health and social care workers can provide and promote inclusion by challenging any discriminatory practice and by promoting inclusive practices.

The 12 ways in which health and social care workers can promote and providing inclusion

1. Principles of care being demonstrated

Agreed ways of working should always be demonstrated and followed. Agreed ways of working include **policies** and **procedures** that health and social care workers are expected to implement and follow. Health and social care workers should be honest and transparent about their role with all individuals they support regarding what they can and cannot offer. By not being honest with individuals from the beginning of the care process, service users may have unrealistic expectations of the care and support that would be provided for them.

2. Agreed ways of working being demonstrated and followed

Implement the appropriate policies and procedures by including and discussing them:

- during team meetings and training courses
- during an appraisal or in a supervised setting
- to establish and maintain an effective working partnership
- when talking to other health and social care colleagues, or to individuals they care for and support
- when receiving feedback from individuals and families they care for and support
- keeping a diary to look back and reflect on how to carry out the work and see if there are different methods of action

Discrimination of any kind can be detrimental to an individual's well-being and may form a barrier to them achieving their desired outcomes. Health and social care workers should avoid discrimination due to the adverse effects it has on individuals. The concept of discrimination is wide-ranging, and it is important that health and social care workers **avoid all types of discrimination**. Discrimination can take many forms within health and social care, such as health and social care workers demonstrating **prejudice**: this means having opinions and thoughts about specific groups of individuals. For example, if a social worker were reluctant to support individuals who have certain religious beliefs, and the social worker does not support their beliefs.

Discriminatory practice can be presented as **providing inadequate care** – for example, not meeting an individual's basic needs, such as not assisting a disabled individual to the toilet when needed. Discriminatory practice can also include all the different types of **abuse** and **neglect**.

Existing good practice could include organising opportunities to agree on adopting good practice during team meetings and training events. Other opportunities could be made available during appraisals or supervision periods or during partnership meetings. Opportunities could also be encouraged when talking to fellow health and social care workers, or during sessions with the patients or clients. This feedback may be enriched by feedback from the families or carers. Another method of promoting inclusion would be to prepare a reflective journal to reflect on current practices and how inclusion could be strengthened.

3. Avoid discrimination by association

Discrimination by association is due to an individual's association with another person belonging to a relevant protected group, such as, for example, by age, disability, gender reassignment, race, religion or belief, sex, and sexual orientation.

It is also important to realise that discrimination can be illegal even if it is against an individual associated with a person belonging to a relevant group, for example, e.g. an employee caring for a disabled child. There was a specific case taken to court, known as the Coleman v Attridge Law (2008), where the parent of a disabled child claimed that they had been treated less favourably by their employer due to the child's disability.

Example of discrimination by association:

- Health and social care workers being annoyed with an individual they are supporting because this person frequently cancels their appointments due to caring for their disabled parent.

4. Avoiding discrimination by perception

Perceptive discrimination is when an individual is discriminated against because he or she is wrongly perceived to have a certain protected characteristic.

Examples of discrimination by perception:

- Refusing to hire an individual with an Arabic name because they are perceived to be associated with Islam.
- Bullying a heterosexual male employee wearing pink because they are perceived to be a homosexual.
- Failing to support an individual with a speech impairment as they are perceived as being mentally disabled.

Discrimination by perception is experienced by many individuals, including Muslim women, who remove their hijabs or to change their names so that they sound more English to avoid discrimination by perception. Research conducted by Vikram Dodd (2012) suggested that prejudice and discrimination are responsible for a quarter of higher unemployment rates, especially for Pakistani and Bangladeshi women.

Activity 1

CASE STUDY – MARC AND ELAINE

Marc has been refused a job in health and social care because he is a carer for his son John, who has a number of disabilities. The organisation has identified that Marc would not be reliable, as he needs to support his son John with his care.

Elaine is a social care assistant. As a result of an accident, she suffered a degree of hearing loss. Elaine applied for promotion and passed the functionality test. However, she was not offered the promotion, as she was informed that she would not be able to perform day-to-day activities in the future due to her disability.

Compare the two types of discrimination being demonstrated and examine the potential effects this may have on the well-being of Marc and Elaine.

Activity 2

CASE STUDY – FLORENCE

Florence is a care worker in a nursing care home. She is currently supporting Gwyn, who has physical and mobility needs. Florence has asked her colleague Seren to assist in helping Gwyn onto the hoist. Seren has turned around and said, "I am so sorry, but I do not agree or respect Gwyn's sexual orientation, so I'm unable to help".

Describe ways that Florence could challenge this discriminatory practice by Seren.

Discrimination can be avoided by health and social care workers and the services they provide by:

- avoiding using 'banter' and inappropriate language with individuals that they are supporting

- attending training and reading up on discrimination by association and perception

- being self-aware and reflective in their practice

- listening to individuals so that they are given a voice.

5. Listening to individuals so that they have a voice

Health and social care workers who listen, stay engaged and can recall information are able to develop trust in their relationships with service users, and are more likely to build a therapeutic relationship with them. Active listening helps the service user to feel valued and understood so they are more likely to talk and communicate effectively. Active listening helps the health and social care workers gain insight into the service user's situation and perspective, so their 'voice' is heard.

6. Equity of access and equal opportunities

Health and social are workers should apply the values of **equality** and respect **diversity** when supporting individuals to achieve their desired outcomes. The concepts of **equality of access** and **equal opportunities** are not merely about being nice to others or treating individuals with respect, even though this is extremely important. Equity of access and equal opportunities involve ensuring that individuals can reach their full potential and have an opportunity to contribute to their communities. Equal opportunities are not about providing the same opportunities for every individual. Equal opportunities mean ensuring that individuals should have opportunities to meet their specific needs, and that individuals are provided with fair and equal access; this ensures service users have the same chance as all other individuals in meeting their desired outcomes.

CASE STUDY – DAFYDD

Dafydd is a community outreach worker. He works alongside local volunteers in the community to organise a weekly event. Currently, Dafydd is looking for a venue, and the event aims to improve the health and well-being of individuals with additional learning needs and individuals with physical disabilities.

Some of the volunteers have never had experience of supporting individuals with additional learning needs and physical disabilities. Dafydd has arranged a meeting with the volunteers to discuss ways in which individuals who attend the weekly event may be supported.

1. Give some examples of how Dafydd and the volunteers can ensure that individuals attending the weekly event are provided with equity of access and equal opportunities.

2. If Dafydd and the volunteers do not provide equity of access and equal opportunities, examine the possible consequences for the individuals who attend the weekly event.

7. Reasonable adjustments

The Equality Act (2010) ensures that individuals should have changes or **reasonable adjustments** made to ensure that they can fully access a range of services, such as for:

- Education
- Employment
- Housing
- Goods and services
- Associations and private clubs

Reasonable adjustments are changes that organisations have to make for individuals who live with disabilities to ensure that they are not disadvantaged in comparison with others who are not disabled. Health and social care workers should be **pro-active** and have an **anticipatory duty** in making reasonable adjustments, meaning health and social care workers should plan in advance to meet the access needs of individuals with disabilities.

Individuals who access health and social care services (which may include statutory services, independent services and third sector services) should not have to pay for any reasonable adjustments to be made in order for them to fully participate in the services. **Charging for reasonable adjustments would be considered as discrimination**. If an individual living with a learning disability or additional need is being supported by a nurse to help them with specialist equipment, there should be some flexibility with the allocated times of the appointment. Some individuals may require a quieter time when there are fewer individuals in the waiting room to wait in. They may have more flexible appointment timings so carers can attend, and public transport services are available.

Reasonable adjustments: the word 'reasonable' is defined as being appropriate or fair or moderate. This definition is open to interpretation, and some other factors may be considered, such as whether the adjustment is:

- physically possible
- practical
- affordable
- likely to harm the health and safety of others

There are other factors that may be considered in terms of whether the adjustment is reasonable such as:

- an individual's specific disability
- if the change required would overcome the disadvantage presented to other disabled service users
- the size of the organisation
- if any changes have already been made

8. Supporting diversity by working in non-judgemental ways

Supporting diversity is a key principle of care for all health and social care workers. Supporting diversity involves accepting and respecting that each individual is **unique** and **different**. This means welcoming individual differences by working in **non-judgemental** ways. Health and social care workers should work in non-judgemental ways, which means they should not make any judgements regarding individual behaviours.

All health and social care workers should work to support individuals by demonstrating a **person-centred approach.** This approach will focus on the likes and dislikes, beliefs, and personal history of each individual to fully respond to the care and support needs of that individual.

How can health and social care staff support diversity by working in non-judgemental ways?

- Recognition of differences, with every individual being seen as different, and their differences valued.

- Activities and resources should reflect different cultures, beliefs, and faiths.

- Celebrate different religious and cultural festivals within the organisation.

- Providing for individual dietary, cultural, religious and mobility needs.

- Specialist meals should be provided as required, for example, halal, kosher, diabetic, gluten-free and vegetarian.

- Ensure that the communication requirements of each individual are met. Information should be given in a range of different formats, including information in braille, hearing loops, interpreters and health and social care staff who can use BSL (British Sign Language) or Makaton (which uses symbols, signs, and speech to enable individuals to communicate).

9. Whistleblowing when appropriate

Health and social care workers often witness a variety of good and bad practices every day. **Whistleblowing** would be appropriate in some situations; for example, in a situation where bad practice has been reported to a supervisor at work, but that bad practice continues to occur. The emphasis will increase to whistleblowing where it appears that no action has been taken to respond to the complaint or request. Another situation would be where a manager is also part of the complaint. In such a situation, it will be necessary to inform an older or senior member of staff within the organisation. In extreme circumstances, health and social care workers should blow the whistle outside the organisation to external authorities such as Healthcare Inspectorate Wales or Care Inspectorate Wales. All health and social care organisations are required to have a whistleblowing policy which provides information on when, why and how to 'blow the whistle'. The policy should also detail the support and safety net available for 'whistleblowers'. Whistleblowers have rights protected by the **Disclosure in the Public Interest Act 1998**, with the Act protecting employees from harmful treatment or persecution by the employer.

It is worth remembering the importance of protecting young members of staff who join the care team. It is important that they also feel confident to report back on an event that does not comply, and their responsibility to look after and protect everyone under their care. This is particularly true if the matter concerns an older member of staff or senior manager within the organisation.

Some examples of poor practice by health and care professionals:

- Any abuse of a child, young person, or adult.
- Concerns not accurately recorded – details changed to protect someone.
- Setting not safeguarding a child – exposing them to unnecessary risks (physical or emotional).
- Risk assessments not being considered.
- Disregard of privacy and dignity during intimate care procedures.
- Inappropriate behaviour from the member of staff.
- Ignoring an individual.
- Verbally abusing an individual.
- Discrimination against a child or family.
- Shouting at or ridiculing an individual.
- Not following correct safety procedures, e.g. not conducting fire drills, incorrect staffing ratios.
- Abuse of authority.
- Malpractice – altering care records.
- Misusing finances – fraud / breaches of financial regulations.

10. Effective communication – ensuring that all contact and communication is clear, using the language and format of the person's choice.

If individuals do not receive communication that is clear and, in the language, and format of their choice, this may result in the patient or client not achieving the best health outcomes. This in turn should provide care that is both safe and effective for all individuals. In Wales, individuals have the right to have health and social care services delivered in Welsh. Under the **Welsh Language (Wales) Measure 2011**, the NHS in Wales has a statutory duty to deliver their services to the public in both Welsh and English. This legislation gives the Welsh language official status in Wales and reinforces the principle that the Welsh language should not be treated less favourably than the English language in Wales. The Welsh Government have also published '**More than just words…**'. This is a Welsh Language Plan for the health and social care sector in which the Welsh Government will embed the Welsh language in health and social care so that people can access the care that they deserve and require. 'More than just words …' is aimed at supporting all staff across NHS Wales in making an '**Active Offer**'. Making an 'Active Offer' is about creating the right environment where patients and clients feel empowered and confident that their needs will be met.

Here are some practical things that can be done to provide an 'Active Offer' in health and social care settings:

I make an 'Active Offer' by greeting people bilingually. Knowing who speaks Welsh in my team means I'm able to ask them for help if a service user needs to speak Welsh.

I provide an 'Active Offer' by greeting service users in Welsh if that's their first language.

I provide an 'Active Offer' by using simple Welsh phrases with service users to make them feel more at ease with the service I'm providing.

I'm providing an 'Active Offer' by having a bilingual service in the food counter area during meals. I'm also making sure that the food menu and the signage is bilingual.

An alternative method to enabling effective communication could be the use of **interpreters** in situations where a team member notices that an individual patient or client has difficulty in speaking English. Under these circumstances, an interpreter may be brought in to help support this individual. This approach would support inclusion, as the individual would be able to be actively involved in his/her care or treatment- a crucial part of inclusive practice.

11. Ensure that no harassment is taking place

Harassment is defined as 'aggressive pressure or intimidation'. Health and social care workers and the services they provide should never humiliate, offend, or degrade an individual. Harassment is never acceptable. Harassment is defined under the law as 'unwanted conduct related to a relevant protected characteristic, which has the purpose or effect of violating an individual's dignity or the creating of an intimidating, hostile, degrading, humiliating or offensive environment for that individual' (Equality Act 2010).

Harassment can affect individuals in many ways, such as:

- Individuals do not feel respected and therefore may not have confidence in being open in relation to any concerns they may have.

- Individuals feel disempowered and do not feel that they are an active partner in their care and support.

- Individuals cannot identify their personal outcomes, as their protected characteristics are not understood.

- Individuals are likely to be socially isolated and excluded, therefore their health may deteriorate.

- Individuals do not feel safe and may be reluctant to report any safeguarding concerns they may have.

AN EXAMPLE OF HARASSMENT: NUHA

Nuha's counsellor Debbie makes a request regarding Nuha's hijab, which is conventionally worn by Muslim women. Nuha has asked Debbie on a number of occasions to stop making remarks about her hijab. Debbie insisted that this was not to offend Nuha, as she did not want Nuha to feel uncomfortable during the counselling session, which was held in a very warm room; she therefore requested Nuha to take off the hijab to make her feel more comfortable.

This is a prime example of harassment. Although Debbie did not want to intentionally offend Nuha, her behaviour was a glaring example of intimidation, since religion is a protected characteristic under the Equality Act 2010.

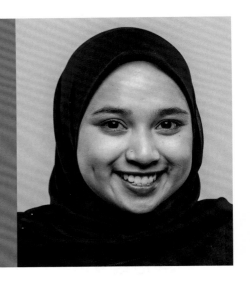

Different types of harassment

Harassment includes a broad range of unwanted behaviour that can lead to emotional distress or harm to individuals. The most common types of harassment include:

- Physical harassment.

- Discriminatory harassment, which includes harassment based on race, religion, gender, or other protected characteristics.

- Psychological harassment, which includes harassment that affects the mental health or well-being of those who are harassed, such as humiliation, manipulation, or isolation.

- Sexual harassment – comments regarding sexual orientation or comments of a sexual nature, such as unkind comments, gestures or advances that create a hostile or offensive environment.

- Personal harassment, which includes bullying, verbal abuse, or intimidation.

For further information om harassment, go to:
https://www.citizensadvice.org.uk/wales/

Activity 4

Prepare an infographic to give to newly qualified health and social care workers on the different types of harassment. Include examples of these different types where possible within health and social care settings and how these occurrences can be avoided.

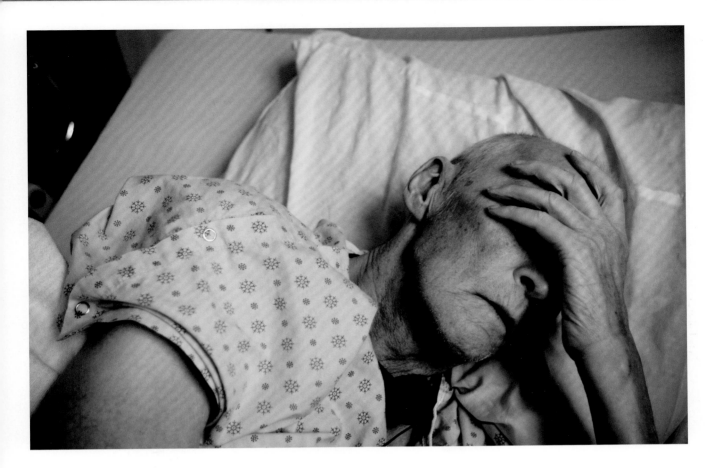

12. Dignity and respect is provided at all times

Health and social care workers should show dignity and respect at all times when supporting individuals. One of the key standards in health and social care is that individuals are treated with respect at all times. **Dignity** is about how individuals think, feel, and behave in relation to the worth or value of themselves and others. Showing **respect** when supporting individuals can ensure that individuals feel a **sense of worth** and feel like an **equal partner**.

How can health and social care workers show respect when dealing with patients and clients?

1   **Active listening** is a method of ensuring that workers listen carefully, listening to what the individual is saying and repeating it back to them to confirm their understanding.

2   Using **inclusive, non-discriminatory language** that avoids stereotypes, prejudices, and stigmatised terms. Stigmatisation is when the language used suggests that specific individuals should be treated unfairly by showing disapproval.

3   Showing interest in their **cultural and religious traditions** and taking part in an appropriate way by celebrating special festivals that are important for them and their community.

Health standards framework

Health and social care workers (and the services that are provided) should treat individuals with dignity and respect to ensure that a quality service is provided in the care setting, the individual's voice is heard and listened to, and that they experience a care system where individuals are treated with compassion and respect.

Dignified care is one of the seven themes stated within the **Health and Care Standards (2015)**. These Health and Care Standards ensure that individuals in Wales using health services or supporting others to do so in a range of health care settings have the right to excellent care, as well as advice and support to maintain their health.

http://www.wales.nhs.uk/sitesplus/documents/1064/24729

http://www.wales.nhs.uk/sitesplus/documents/1064/24729_Health%20Standards%20Framework_2015_E1.pdf

Activity 5

CASE STUDY – ADELE

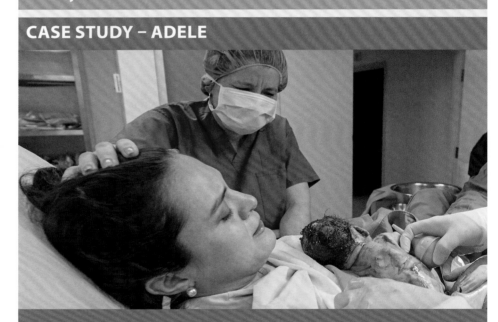

Adele is a midwife, and she has been supporting Justine, who has given birth for the first time. Justine had a Caesarean section, and is currently recovering from the operation. Justine is French and has only been living in Wales for twelve months, so she does not have family members to support her in Wales. She is vegan, which means she does not eat or use products derived from animals.

However, since the Caesarean section, Justine is struggling to move, and therefore will probably require a bed bath. Adele has also been supporting Justine with breast feeding and her other needs.

Explain how Adele can treat Justine to promote inclusion.

A summary of the methods that a health and social care worker can follow to promote inclusion in terms of their duties in their workplace

- Demonstrate principles of care and follow agreed procedures.

- Focus on implementing good practice within the health and social care setting.

- Ensure that methods of communication are always clear, using the preferred language and procedures that the patient wishes.

- Make sure that:

  - there is no discrimination by association – that is, the association between one individual and another individual who belongs to a relevant protected group such as age, disability, gender reassignment, race, religion or belief, gender, and sexual orientation.

  - there is no discrimination by perception – that is, discrimination against someone due to a mistaken perception that the person has a specific protected characteristic.

- Prevent harassment that is aggressive pressure or intimidation.

- Challenge any discriminatory practice and promote inclusive practice.

- Provide fair access by ensuring equal and appropriate opportunities for all without adopting a one-size-fits-all approach, and making reasonable adjustments as appropriate.

- Adopt a positive attitude and approach in relation to supporting individuals to ensure they are not excluded or isolated.

- Know when it is appropriate to 'blow the whistle'.

- Listen to individuals to ensure that they always have their say and that their voice is heard.

- Support diversity by accepting and welcoming what makes an individual different, using non-judgmental methods.

- Treat everyone with dignity and respect.

Reading and further research

Protected characteristics
https://www.citizensadvice.org.uk/wales/

Whistleblowing
http://www.gov.uk/whistleblowing

'Active Offer'
**https://socialcare.wales/cms_assets/file-uploads/150928activeoffersoci
alservicesen.pdf**

Harassment
https://www.citizensadvice.org.uk/wales/

Health and Care Standards (2015)
**http://www.wales.nhs.uk/sitesplus/documents/1064/24729_ Health%20
Standards%20Framework_2015_E1.pdf**

https://heiw.nhs.wales/

What is Stigma? | Time to Change Wales
**https://www.timetochangewales.org.uk/en/mental-health-stigma/
what-stigma/**

ACTIVITY ANSWERS
Activity 1: Marc and Elaine

With reference to Marc and Elaine, compare the two types of discrimination being demonstrated and examine the potential effects this may have had on the well-being of Marc and Elaine.

Marc has been discriminated against by association, as he was associated with his son John, who has disabilities, whereas Elaine has been discriminated against by perception, as she was believed to have a disability.

The potential effects of discrimination on the lives of Marc and Elaine:

- Poor health and well-being (any reference to well-being would be useful).
- Low self-esteem and low self-confidence.
- Unfair treatment, which can lead to disempowerment.
- Mental health could suffer.
- Human needs are being blocked.
- Life chances restricted.
- Relationship breakdown.
- Social isolation.

ACTIVITY ANSWERS
Activity 2: Florence

Describe ways that Florence could challenge this discriminatory practice by Seren.

It is essential to challenge discrimination every time. It will be necessary to respond to all forms of discrimination whenever it takes place. Here are some of the actions that a health and social care worker will need to consider and implement:

- **At the time of the discrimination taking place** – Florence should have immediately challenged her colleague about discriminatory behaviour by explaining to Seren that it is both unlawful and unethical to behave in this manner, and that such actions are discriminatory.

- **Challenge the discrimination through procedures** – Florence could have referred the incident to her superior/manager and referred to the care home Equal Opportunities Policy. By referring this incident to the manager, awareness of the discrimination is raised, and it may be recommended that the health and social care worker Seren receives additional training in equality and inclusive practice. This would make it clear that this sort of discriminatory behaviour will not be tolerated. The manager should also ask the health and social care worker Seren to apologise to the service user Gwyn.

■ **Florence could challenge Seren's behaviour straight after the event** – Florence could refer to the codes of practice of the organisation and follow the instructions, investigating the disciplinary action against the health and social care worker – making them aware of the the disciplinary action against the health and social care worker – making them aware of the seriousness of the issue, providing a basis for changing individual's attitudes and consulting with senior health and social care workers to address the issue.

■ **Florence could challenge the behaviour through long-term proactive campaigning** – this could take the form of providing awareness sessions about sexual orientation and equality. On this basis, Florence could discuss the issues with Seren so that she understands the requirements and is ready to implement the relevant legislation, standards and codes of practice and procedure. Holding staff training sessions would also be an effective means of creating awareness for everyone in the team responsible for health and social care. Discrimination is often more effectively challenged through a regular proactive training programme and implementing good practice. This will also offer a good opportunity not only to highlight the requirements of the current legislation, but also to reflect the requirements of new legislation. Challenging discrimination over the years has led to changes in legislation. For example, campaigns against gender differences have led to the legalisation of mixed orientation and gay marriage.

ACTIVITY ANSWERS
Activity 3: Dafydd

1. Give some examples of how Dafydd and the volunteers can ensure that individuals attending the weekly event are provided with equity of access and equal opportunities.

■ Adaptations to improve access such as avoiding steps, stairs, ensuring doorways are not too narrow, good wheelchair access, parking spaces and toilets for disabled people and easy access to buildings and moving within the building.

■ Information provided in different formats, e.g. braille, large print, BSL, Makaton.

■ Hearing loop provided.

■ Volunteers trained in manual handling.

■ Making sure that volunteers have positive attitudes towards enabling equal opportunities.

■ Provide information and positive statements about the equal opportunities provided by the establishment and the organisation.

■ Provide evidence that legislation and codes of practice relating to equal opportunities are active within the organisation. For example, the ethos and the legislation included within the Equality Act 2010.

2. Examine the possible consequences for the individuals who attend the weekly event if Dafydd and the volunteers do not provide equity of access and equal opportunities.

■ Individuals may avoid using the service – individuals may become socially isolated and not trust the volunteers.

■ Depression – individuals could become depressed, as they are not supported effectively to participate in community events.

■ Stressed – individuals could experience anxiety and upset caused by the way they have been treated, and they could become ill.

ACTIVITY ANSWERS
Activity 5: Adele

Explain how Adele can treat Justine to promote inclusion.

Specifically, when giving Justine the bed bath, Adele should promote inclusion by treating her as a unique individual, with dignity and respect, by:

■ Closing the curtains while carrying out a bed bath procedure or when Justine is breastfeeding.

■ Adele realising that curtains are not soundproof, so therefore if Justine is not in her own room, making sure that she talks quietly and does not say anything that could or would embarrass Justine.

■ Making sure that when undertaking a bed bath, Adele has everything that she needs to wash and dry.

■ Trying to encourage Justine to be more independent, in preparation for life as a mother without her family around to support her.

■ Communicating with Justine throughout the whole wash, as it is very intimidating and embarrassing.

■ Making sure that Justine is covered on the upper body when washing the lower body, and vice versa.

■ Using privacy pegs on the curtains when washing Justine to ensure others don't just walk in.

General practice to promote Justine's inclusion should include:

■ Ensuring the principles of care and agreed working practices are upheld and followed in the hospital.

■ Ensuring clear and effective communication, especially since English is Justine's additional language.

- Ensuring there is no discrimination directed towards Justine.

- Providing equity of access and making reasonable adjustments to avoid a one-size fits all. Justine is vegan, so appropriate food must be provided for her to eat.

- Supporting Justine's individual characteristics in a non-judgemental way and treating her with dignity and respect.

- Making sure that Justine is not excluded or isolated, and therefore feels included.

Unit 6

Working in the health and social care sector

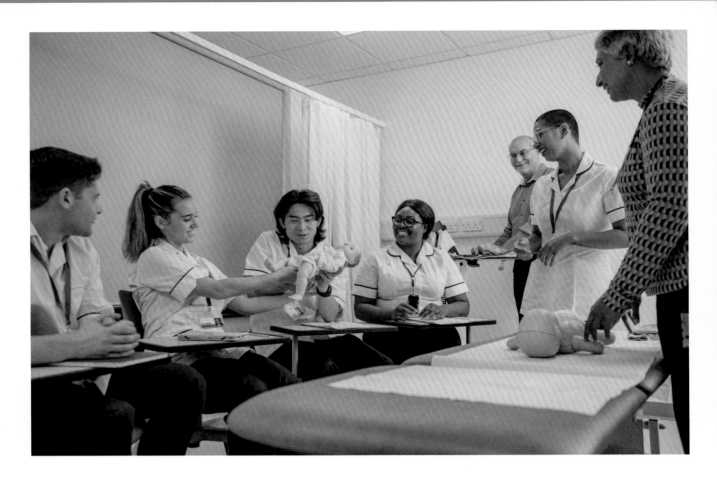

Unit 6: Introduction

Working in the health and social care sector

In this unit, you will build on your knowledge and understanding of working in the health and social care sector – through classroom teaching, and by having a work experience placement (minimum 100 hours, which must include at least 60 hours on work placement). Where possible, we encourage you to experience a minimum of two settings during your sector engagement.

This unit is internally assessed and then externally moderated by WJEC. There is a non-examination assessment (NEA), containing tasks set by WJEC and based on the learners' sector engagement and work placement. You should become aware of the assessment criteria for this NEA, which has fixed tasks, and the assessment will remain the same for the lifetime of the specification.

Non-Examination Assessment (NEA)

■ A work experience placement of at least 60 hours, and classroom teaching of at least 40 hours, will provide you with knowledge and understanding of working in the health and social care sector.

■ Assessed through fixed assignment tasks set by WJEC to investigate a setting/service that provides health and social care services within Wales.

■ Working under supervised conditions, you will have 18 hours to produce your evidence.

■ A reflective diary and sector engagement record from the work experience placement needs to be submitted for moderation.

■ You can also refer to sides of A4 optional notes, if required, and these must be submitted for moderation.

■ This assessment contributes 15% of the overall qualification grade for the Diploma.

■ You are encouraged to experience two settings during your sector engagement.

■ You have to sign a declaration confirming that plagiarism or the use of AI has not taken place in the production of your NEA report. This means that you must not copy information directly from sources, without using quotation marks and stating the source used. If plagiarism or the use of AI is evident, your NEA work will be classed as malpractice and may not be awarded any marks.

Assessment objectives (AOs)

Assessment objective	% That you will be assessed on
AO1 – Demonstrate knowledge and understanding of a range of key concepts, values, and issues that are relevant to health and social care	30%
AO2 – Apply knowledge and understanding of health and social care principles and contexts.	37%
AO3 – Analyse and evaluate health and social care theories and practice to demonstrate understanding, reflect on how they can influence practice, making reasoned judgements and drawing conclusions.	33%

Assignment command verbs

Assignment section	Command word	Requirements of response
Section A (i) (ii) Section C (ii)	Outline	Set out the main points/ provide a brief description or main characteristics
Section A (iii)	Consider	Review and respond to given information
Section B	Examine	Investigate closely, in detail
Section C (i) Section E Section F	Explain	Provide details and reasons for how and why something is the way it is
Section D	Analyse	Examine an issue in detail/ how parts relate to whole, to explain and interpret

Your work placement(s) must be in a health or a social care setting/ service. Settings appropriate for work/observational/shadowing placements could include:

- NHS hospital and community services

- County council social services/well-being departments

- Housing services or social housing services

- Day centres – older adults or learning disability

- Nursing and care homes

- Hospices or palliative care services

- Family centres

- Food banks

- Special educational needs units – **not mainstream school**

- Charities (MIND, British Heart Foundation, Macmillan, local health/social care-related charities) – **not charity shops for an appropriate setting**

- Sports activities where there is a focus on health and care values.

Sector engagement/work placement record and reflective diary

The reflective diary and sector engagement record from the work placement will also need to be submitted for moderation. Your reflective diary therefore will be vital for this assignment.

In completing this sector engagement record, you should concisely summarise the activity undertaken, the date the activity took place and the duration in hours. Your sector engagement record must be submitted for moderation.

You must keep a reflective diary throughout your sector engagement and work placement experience. This should include information on:

- the types of organisations and services that you have engaged with and undertaken work placement with

- the types of tasks and activities that you have undertaken on a daily basis whilst on work placement

- any problems and obstacles that you have encountered and actions you took to overcome them.

▲ Sector engagement and work placement record available from the qualification page of the Consortium website (www. healthandcarelearning.wales)

You must provide a reflective diary when you submit your assignment:

You will be encouraged to complete a daily entry during your work experience. Your tutor will also encourage you to complete your diary entries through regular, short, in-class discussions to enable you to reflect on the experiences and care practices observed in the setting. You should also complete a diary entry on your wider sector engagement experiences, such as following a visit by a guest speaker etc.

The reflective diary should directly demonstrate how the content of the unit can be applied to your selected health or social care setting(s). You should be familiar with the NEA assessment question, and content guidance to ensure that you gather the necessary information from your work experience placement. The requirements of the diary include:

- Job roles, qualifications and skills needed by health and social care workers.
- The role of effective communication, co-production, collaboration, teamwork, and professionalism in the care sector.
- How codes of conduct and practice are adhered to and applied in health and social care settings.
- Safeguarding in practice.
- How different approaches in various settings are used to meet individuals' needs and requirements.
- How Welsh legislation impacts practice in health and social care settings.

The purpose of the work experience is for you to:

- gain first-hand experience of working conditions in different health or social care settings
- find out information about a range of careers in health and social care by shadowing individuals in various roles
- learn, apply, and practise some of the basic skills needed to work in a health and/or social care setting, such as communication skills
- develop skills in assessing your own talents, and to gain confidence and responsibility
- understand the role of multi-disciplinary working practices
- understand the appropriate legislation in health and social care.

Further research and information gathering

Whilst undertaking sector engagement/work experience, you must be encouraged to:

- write an account of the of activities seen and undertaken whilst in the setting work experience, and reflect on what you learnt from the experience. For example, you may have observed and taken part in an excellent example of a reminiscence therapy session in a care home. However, you should think and reflect back on the effect this may have had on a service user, or how the activity was communicated to service users.

- reflect how care values are demonstrated in the setting.

- reflect on how the service users may feel in the environment.

- observe how all employees in the setting contribute to ensuring that service users meet their personal outcomes, whilst identifying the key qualities of each health and/or social care role in the setting.

- ask members of the team about their roles in the setting, and document this, too.

- interact with other members of the multi-disciplinary team in the setting, which may include visiting physiotherapists, occupational therapists, pharmacists, dieticians etc. On reflection, learners should be noting in their diaries who had an input on the care of the service user, and how they did so.

- consider how members of the multi-disciplinary team work together effectively to ensure service user personal outcomes are achieved.

Specification content:

Assignment content mapping	Chapter reference
6.1 Job roles, qualifications and skills needed by health and social care workers	**Chapter 1** ■ Who works within health and social care? ■ How are health and social care workers regulated? ■ Which qualifications are relevant to specific job roles? ■ What skills are needed to work within health and social care?
6.2 The role of effective communication, co-production, collaboration, teamwork, and professionalism in the care sector.	**Chapter 2** ■ How are certain skills demonstrated within the health and social care sector? ■ How do skills support the care workers and the individuals?
6.3 How codes of conduct/practice are adhered to and applied in health and social care settings	**Chapter 3** ■ What are codes of conduct and professional practice? ■ How are codes of conduct/practice adhered to and applied? ■ What are trade unions?
6.4 Role of employers in promoting and protecting the rights of the employee.	**Chapter 4** ■ How do employers promote and protect the rights of the employees working within health and social care? ■ What is the role of legislation? ■ What does duty of care mean?
6.5 Safeguarding in practice.	**Chapter 5** ■ How can safeguarding in practice be achieved? ■ What happens if safeguarding procedures and policies are breached?
6.6 How approaches in settings are used to meet individuals' needs and requirements.	**Chapter 6** ■ How are different approaches used in settings to meet individuals' needs?
6.7 How Welsh legislation impacts practice in health and social care settings	**Chapter 7** ■ How Welsh legislation impacts practice in health and social care. ■ How inspectorates and regulators ensure professional standards and guidance are adhered to.
6.8 The role of reflection in care settings	**Chapter 8** ■ What is reflective practice? ■ Who are reflective practice theorists? ■ How does reflection improve health and social care practice? ■ How does reflective practice take place in health and social care?

Non-Examination Assessment Task 1 A(i)

> **Write an introduction about the setting /service!**
>
> ■ **The main purpose of the chosen setting/service**
>
> ■ **The role of the employer in promoting and protecting the rights of employees working in the setting/service**

Answers must outline the main purpose of the setting/service directly experienced as part of sector engagement and could include:

■ Anti-discrimination and anti-harassment practices

■ Promoting equality

■ Health and safety principles

■ Policies and procedures

■ Initiatives and strategies

■ Confidentiality and social media policies

■ Legislation: Well-being of Future Generations Act 2015, GDPR

■ Duty of care with a focus on health and well-being

■ Holistic, comprehensive, and supportive culture

N.B. The specification content for the role of the employer in promoting and protecting the rights of employees working in the setting or service is found in Chapter 6.4.

What are examiners looking for?

■ The Non-Examination Assessment (NEA) needs to use a clear and organised written format, and usually addresses each task in a logical order.

■ It is necessary to demonstrate thorough knowledge and understanding of the content of the specification and its application to a location or service experienced during the work experience.

■ Need to highlight and draw attention to the good practice or practices experienced during the experience by citing sources used in your reports.

■ Prepare a general bibliography to show evidence of the research you have done by researching other sources through reading and further research on the web.

■ You will lose marks if you do not refer, in detail, to the role of the employer, or do not refer appropriately to the location or the service.

■ Avoid plagiarism – do not copy information directly from secondary sources, without using quotation marks and citing the source used. The use of AI is also prohibited and regarded as plagiarism. If plagiarism is evident, then your NEA work will be considered as malpractice and many not receive any marks.

6.1: Job roles, qualifications and skills needed by health and social care workers

This chapter looks at the jobs within the health and social care sector, the qualifications and skills needed, and how they are regulated. The information from this chapter, together with the research gathered from your sector engagement and work experience, will provide you with the information required in preparing your assignment.

Who works within the health and social care sector?

Allied health professional	People who provide distinct types of health care who are not doctors, nurses, or pharmacists. This description includes a wide range of professional roles, including physiotherapists, occupational therapists, dietitians, podiatrists, and others.
Practitioner	A person who works in a skilled job such as social work, nursing, or medicine, providing care or support directly to people.

Although individuals in Wales will use health and social care services throughout their lives, they may not be aware of how many people work within these services. In fact, health and social care services employ a substantial number of people in a wide range of job roles.

NHS Cymru employs about 100,000 people in over 300 distinct roles, supporting a population of over 3 million individuals of all ages in Wales. The total number of directly employed NHS staff continues to rise. The NHS actually employs more people in Wales than any other organisation.

https://www.bbc.co.uk/news/uk-wales-44482582

https://www.gov.wales/staff-directly-employed-nhs

Social Care Wales employs about 70,000 people in a wide range of roles, supporting around 150,000 individuals

Gofal Cymdeithasol **Cymru**
Social Care **Wales**

of all ages every year in Wales. This results in a wide range of job roles working in social care in Wales.

Health and care skills

Separate roles within health and social care settings and services will require specific skills to enable staff to fulfil the requirements of their roles successfully.

These skills include:

- excellent and effective communication
- ability to adapt
- remaining professional at all times
- accuracy
- organising skills and following instructions
- prioritising tasks
- compassion
- empathy
- knowing when to ask for help
- IT skills
- problem-solving skills
- time management skills
- resilience
- decision-making skills
- teamwork.

Frontline care and support functions

Job roles within health and social care are divided into two categories, namely **frontline care** (providing care for individuals) and **support functions** (management, administrative and support staff).

Roles in frontline care	Roles in support functions
Ambulance teams / paramedics	Estates and facilities
Healthcare support workers	Publicity and information services
Care workers	Managerial
Social workers	Finance
Medical	Administration
Nursing	Human resources
Allied health professionals	Catering and cleaning
Activities workers	Domestic help
Personal assistants	Reception and appointments
Rehabilitation worker	Porter and ancillary worker
Domiciliary carers	Advice and assistance worker
Physiotherapists	

Gathering information during your work experience to record staff numbers, job roles, and the qualifications required within the location or service

When visiting your location or service in the health and social care sector, you will need to record the number of people employed there, and the nature of the jobs within that location or service. You will also need to say if the location is one that offers frontline services, or a location that offers support functions.

To gather this information, you could:

 ask your employer for a list of the distinct roles within the setting

 prepare a list of the different job roles that you have observed or worked alongside

 prepare a list which shows which team members have frontline care responsibilities, and those team members that have support functions and responsibilities.

How are health and social care workers regulated?

Certain job roles within health and social are regulated. Each individual must, therefore, conform with these requirements so that they are able to practise. All workers must be registered with a regulated body and hold relevant qualifications, which might include a degree or diploma.

Professional bodies

An organisation that represents a group of people who are members of the same profession, such as doctors or social workers. A professional body supports its members, with some professional bodies stipulating that members reflect the mandatory requirements of the professional body.

Healthcare Inspectorate Wales

Healthcare Inspectorate Wales inspects NHS services and regulates independent healthcare providers, in relation to a number of standards, policies and guidelines in Wales. The Inspectorate also has a statutory duty, through a number of recognised regulations, to highlight areas and practices that need improvement.

Care Inspectorate Wales (CIW)

To safeguard the well-being of the people of Wales, Care Inspectorate Wales registers, inspects, and implements the necessary actions that are required to improve the quality and safety of services.

Activity

Use various sources, including online research, to prepare a list of the main duties of the following roles within the health and social care service. You can expand this list by including your own experience of observing or collaborating with individuals who carry out these duties during your engagement or practice.

- Nurse
- Midwife
- Social worker
- Healthcare worker
- Social care worker
- Art therapist
- Biomedical scientist
- Chiropodist/podiatrist
- Clinical scientist
- Dietician
- Audiologist
- Occupational therapist
- Operating department practitioner
- Orthoptist
- Paramedic
- Physiotherapist
- Pharmacist
- Chiropractor
- Dentist
- Dental hygienist

Health and social care organisations and regulatory bodies

The Health and Care Professions Council (HCPC)	The role of the HCPC is to protect the public. By law, people must be registered to work in the health and social care sector in the UK. This organisation regulates 15 professions within the sector to set and maintain standards. For example, a social worker must be registered with the HCPC to practise as a social worker. The registered professions include social workers, healthcare workers, social care workers, arts therapists, biomedical scientists, chiropodists/podiatrists, clinical scientists, dietitians, hearing-aid dispensers, occupational therapists, operating department practitioners, orthoptists, paramedics, and physiotherapists.
The General Medical Council (GMC)	The GMC holds a medical register for all doctors in the UK, stating their registration details and training information. Doctors who practise medicine in the UK must hold a registration with the GMC, which gives them a licence to practise.
The Nursing & Midwifery Council (NMC)	An independent regulator for nurses, midwives, specialist public health nurses and nursing associates. The NMC holds a register of all nurses and midwives who can practise in the UK.
The General Chiropractic Council	Regulates all chiropractors in the UK and ensures the safety of patients getting treatment.
The General Dental Council	Regulates dentists and dental care professionals in the UK. It sets dental standards, and holds a register of qualified dentists and other dental care professionals such as dental hygienists, dental therapists, dental nurses, dental technicians and clinical dental technicians.
The General Optical Council	This organisation maintains a register of its professionals, and regulates the services provided by opticians and optometrists. It promotes exacting standards of professional conduct and continual education and training opportunities.
The General Pharmaceutical Council	Regulates pharmacists, pharmacy technicians and pharmacy premises in the UK.

Social care regulatory bodies

Care Inspectorate Wales	This organisation registers, inspects and takes action to improve the quality and safety of services in Wales. Care Inspectorate Wales regulates the following social care services: ■ Adult services such as in care homes for adults and domiciliary support services. ■ Children's services, such as in care homes for children, fostering and adoption services. ■ Childcare and play services, such as for childminders and full day care workers.
Social Care Wales	This organisation works with the Welsh Government to improve outcomes for people who use care and support services in Wales. The aims and objectives of Social Care Wales include: ■ Prepare and implement improvements to social care in Wales. ■ Provide a register of adult care home workers in Wales. ■ Provide guidance for employers about the registration process for their workers. ■ Support and develop a high-quality and skilled workforce by improving care and support provision and increasing public confidence in care services in Wales.

The primary roles of regulatory bodies include:

1   The preparation of a registration process and register for all health and social care workers, so that they comply with each specific regulatory body.

2   That all health and social care workers have the relevant qualifications required. This will enable all health and social care workers to be able to undertake their role with confidence and competence.

3   Set mandatory and discretionary standards, ensuring that all health and social care workers comply with the standards.

4   Investigate all complaints made against registered health or social care workers.

Which qualifications are required for specific job roles?

Specific job roles within the health and social care sector require that you have the relevant qualifications. These may include:

- GCSEs
- Vocational qualifications
- A levels
- Diplomas
- Undergraduate degree
- Postgraduate degree

There are certain job roles within the health and social care sector that only need one or some of these qualifications. However, other job roles will require higher level qualifications and years of training. There are also opportunities for individuals to gain qualifications whilst working in the service or setting. These can be through apprenticeships, graduate learning programmes and/or traineeships. It is the responsibility of the regulatory body to ensure that each health and social care worker has the appropriate qualifications to perform their job role.

Gathering information during your sector engagement or during your work experience placement:

1. Gathering information about membership of professional bodies

Once you have collected the information about the job roles within your setting, you will also need details of which regulatory bodies require their registration.

You can gather this information:

 by asking the care worker with which professional body they have registered

 by online research about which organisation regulates a specific job role or job roles

2. Gathering information about qualifications of the team in a location or service

During your visit to a setting, you will need to gather information about the necessary qualifications required for **at least two roles** within a setting or service.

You can gather this information:

 by interviewing a member/members of staff and asking for their qualifications, and whether there are specific qualifications that are required for their own particular job role

 online research for the qualifications required for specific job roles

3. Gathering information about skills of the team in a location or a service

During your visit to a setting, you will need to gather information about the necessary skills required for **at least two roles** within a setting or service.

You can gather this information:

 by observing them during the practice and gaining an insight into their skills

 by interviewing staff members to find out which skills they use, and how they use them, in their job role

Checklist for your assignment

In preparation for your assignment, you must ensure that you have sourced comprehensive information about your setting or service that will enable you to:

 outline in detail two job roles within, or related to, the setting or the service

 outline in detail the main functions of the role

 outline in detail the specific skills required

 outline in detail the qualification requirements

 outline in detail how the role is professionally regulated

Non-Examination Assessment Task A(ii)

> **Outline two job roles within, or related to, the setting or the service, to include:**
>
> ■ **The main purpose of the role**
>
> ■ **Specific skills required**
>
> ■ **Qualification requirements**
>
> ■ **Professional regulation as appropriate to the role**

Getting started!

You will need to research the **two** health and social care roles you have chosen for this assessment. Your research will need to include information about the two roles you have seen at your work experience placement within the health and social care sector. During this time, you will need to gather detailed information about the two roles, in addition to keeping notes in your reflective diary.

You will also need to do additional research by using various sources of information, such as printed publications and by searching the internet. There are many sources of information available online which provide detailed information of different roles within the health and social care sector.

Your engagement research and the additional information could also be used to prepare the two sides of A4 notes, which you can take with you to the controlled assessment.

The roles of the care worker

There is a wide range of jobs available within the health and social care sector. Each one of these jobs will have different roles to play within the health and social care sector. These roles will either need qualifications, or in certain roles, no specific qualifications. Here are some of the role requirements of working as a care worker:

The main roles of the care worker include:

- Providing high-quality personal care and support to residents living within care settings with everyday tasks (dependent on the abilities of the individuals that they care for).

- Encouraging patients and clients to maintain independence and to be socially active within the setting. Preparing and delivering a care and support plan within the setting which will be evaluated on a regular basis to ensure that personal health and care provision is delivered in a caring and supportive way.

- To actively engage with individuals in conversation and meaningful occupational tasks related to their lifestyle choices, at a level and pace that values the individual and respects their dignity and communication differences.

- Assisting residents during mealtimes, ensuring they receive meals that reflect their dietary requirements while promoting well-being and an active lifestyle. Assisting with ensuring that care plans are regularly reviewed and updated, and that they are appropriate to the needs of everyone. Reviewing practices and procedures and adopting 'best practice' methods.

- Care workers are often working within a Multi-disciplinary Team (MDT) that includes a broad range of professions and expertise to provide a unified and seamless service, to ensure that individuals are receiving the appropriate care and support that they deserve.

Qualification requirements

To work as a care worker in Wales, you need the following qualifications:

1   Level 3 qualification in Health and Social Care (Diploma, QCF, NVQ or BTEC) or equivalent.

2   Alternatively, you can register using the City & Guilds Level 2 Health and Social Care: Core, but you will need to complete the full Level 3 qualification within three years.

3   Recommended qualifications for practice include City & Guilds Level 3 Health and Social Care: Practice (Children and young people).

4   If you do not have social care qualifications, you can still work in certain roles and complete your qualifications as you work.

Important personal characteristics:

- Patience.

- The ability to adapt.

- Excellent communication and interpersonal skills.

- A willingness to talk and listen to people from all backgrounds.

- A commitment to work with other team members in the Multi-disciplinary Team.

- Enthusiastic about providing the best care and support to patients and clients under your care.

- Respecting the right of each individual to independence and privacy.

- A commitment to adopt a person-centred approach, and to understand and value that each individual has different physical and emotional needs.

- Able to ease an individual's embarrassment when you help them with personal care.

- A commitment to provide a social care service which enshrines an individual's dignity and their right to be treated with respect.

- A willingness to learn and adopt new practices and procedures in line with new legislation, standards, and codes of practice.

Professional regulation of care workers:

Care Inspectorate Wales (CIW) regulates social care support services. Regulation includes registration, inspection, responding to concerns about regulated services, compliance, support and enforcement.

What the examiner is looking for

1   Your answer must include two appropriate job roles from within, or related to, the setting or the service from your engagement setting.

2   You will need to provide detailed information about requirements in terms of qualifications and professional regulation.

Reading and further research

Careers Wales **www.careerswales.com**

NHS Wales **https://www.nhs.wales/**

NHS Wales Careers **https://heiw.nhs.wales/careers/nhs-wales-careers/**

Social Care Wales Qualification Framework **https://socialcare.wales/qualifications-funding/qualification-framework**

Skills for Care **https://socialcare.wales/training-modules-and-courses-for-care-workers**

6.2: The role of effective communication, co-production, collaboration, teamwork, and professionalism in the care sector

This chapter looks at the role of effective communication, co-production, collaboration, teamwork, and professionalism in the care sector. The information in this chapter and the research gathered from your sector engagement and/or work experience will provide examples of the role of effective communication which may have been demonstrated within the setting.

How does effective communication play a role in providing quality care?

Effective communication plays a vital role in providing quality care and support to improve well-being outcomes for individuals. Care workers are expected to effectively communicate with individuals to determine their care and support needs and solve any problems in a proactive manner.

Communication in health and social care settings is used to:

- find out the service users' physical, intellectual, emotional, social and language needs
- establish robust relationships
- give and obtain information
- diagnose
- check on the progress of the users of the services
- provide support, comfort, and reassurance.

All service users have different ways of communicating with service users. This difference reflects on what works best for all parties. All service users have the right to choose their preferred method of building relationships or their preferred choice of language.

Effective communication is needed to ensure that high-quality care and support is provided for all service users in Wales. By using effective communication, care workers can develop trusting relationships with service users, which will help address their needs and overall health, well-being, and resilience.

Types of communication

Written	letters, policies, emails, records
Verbal	speaking, singing, active listening
Non-verbal	body language, gestures, mime and drama, music, art, and craft
Graphical	posters, signs, symbols, and diagrams
Alternative methods of communication	British Sign Language (BSL), Makaton, Braille, Widget

Some service users may:

- speak different languages
- have limited vision or hearing loss
- find it difficult to speak and/or may have limited understanding of what is being said.

Therefore, it is important for the care worker to remember that communication can be affected due to a number of factors:

- **Visual impairments** affect a service user's ability to understand written communication and body language.

- **Hearing impairments** affect a service user's speaking and listening ability.

- **Cognitive ability** affects a service user's concentration and thinking abilities.

- **Special educational needs** may limit verbal and written communication ability.

- **Physical disabilities** may affect a service user's writing ability, or they may need to use technology to aid communication.

It is important for health and social care workers to consider the following information to **ensure** that effective communication takes place:

Verbal communication	<ul><li>When speaking, the need to be aware of the tone, pitch, speed, and volume of voice used, as this could alter how the messages are received by the service user.</li><li>Avoid the use of jargon or abbreviations and complicated words and terminology.</li><li>Always speak in a respectful way, adjusting speech to suit the individual.</li><li>Active listening, which involves checking for understanding, is really important for effective communication.</li><li>Silence can be used to encourage another individual to talk and to fill in the conversation gaps. Silence can also be used to show empathy and concern for another person's feelings.</li></ul>
Sign language	This is a globally recognised language which is a visual means of communicating using gestures, facial expression, and body language. British Sign Language (BSL) is used by people living with deafness or hearing impairments.
Makaton	This is a form of language that uses a large collection of signs and symbols. Makaton is often used by individuals living with learning and physical disabilities or with a hearing impairment.
Braille	This system can support reading and writing for individuals living with visual impairment or blindness. It Is a code of raised dots that are 'read' using touch.
Body language	This is a type of non-verbal communication. There are many different aspects of body language, including gestures, facial expressions, eye contact, body positioning and body movements. Body language can communicate information about an individual or a worker, often without them realising it.
Gestures	These are hand or arm movements emphasising what is being said; they can be used as an alternative to speaking. Facial expressions support what is being said by showing reactions or feelings, and give valuable clues about a person's emotions.
Eye contact	Maintaining good eye contact is an important way for a worker to show that they are engaged and listening.

Position	The way a person stands, sits, or holds their arms when talking will provide others with clues about that person's feelings, attitude, and emotions.
Written communication	This method is used to send messages, communicate, keep records, or provide evidence.

Effective communication in your sector engagement/work experience placement

Whilst undertaking your sector engagement placement, you will need to observe and identify the different types of communication being used.

You could:

 observe care workers and identify the communication methods being used.

 make a list of the different reasons or needs, to explain why the different communication methods are being used.

What is co-production?

▲ Co-production – working together for better care

Co-production is one of the main principles of the Social Services and Well-being (Wales) Act 2014. It means working in partnership with and involving each individual, their family, friends, and carers to make sure that they receive high-quality care and the necessary support systems.

Co-production encourages the involvement and engagement of people in Wales to create public policies and services for the health and social care sector. Both health and social care professionals and the people of Wales need to work together to plan and support best practice within a high-quality service delivery framework. Co-production is a way of working where practitioners and people work together as equal partners to plan and deliver care and support.

The advantages of co-production include:

- recognition that people (service users and their families) are **assets** with a positive and essential contribution to make

- viewing service users, their families, and carers as **equal partners** in the planning, developing, and accessing of care and support

- providing the **opportunity to make the best use of individual capabilities** to get the best outcomes

- encouraging the development of **community networks** for the sharing of information

- encouraging **co-operation** and **effective communication** between health and social care practitioners and a range of people, by the sharing of their views and beliefs, leading to actions to produce successful working relationships

- supporting and **empowering** people to get **involved** with the design and operation of services

- empowering people to **take responsibility** for, and contribute to, their own well-being

- ensuring that practitioners work in **partnership** with people to achieve well-being outcomes at an individual and a whole-service level

- blurring distinctions between providers and people who need care and support and **carers who need support**

- promoting more **feedback** opportunities for service users and their families and carers by involving people in designing outcomes for services

- supporting the delivery of **person-centred care**, ensuring service users, their families and carers are at the centre of all planning and decision-making.

Gathering information about co-production during your sector engagement or your work experience placement

Whilst undertaking your sector engagement placement, you will need to identify and explain how **co-production** is carried out within the setting.

You could:

 ask the employer

 speak to the service users or residents

 interview the care workers

What is collaboration and teamwork?

Collaboration is the basis of success in any team. When health and social care providers work in collaboration, individual outcomes and quality of care tend to improve. It involves not only the service user and the care workers, but also their families and carers, working together. Collaboration involves a team of care workers using their knowledge and ideas of what needs to be done or improved, to help a service user's health, well-being, and resilience.

Teamwork in health and social care brings together people with different skills, abilities, and talents to provide the best possible care and treatment for individuals.

Multi-disciplinary team	'Multi-disciplinary team' refers to when a group of care professionals work together to support a service user and their needs. Each member of the team will have their own specific set of skills, that contribute towards at least one aspect of the service user's needs.
Multi-agency working	'Multi-agency working' refers to settings and/or organisations working together to deliver services to service users who may have multiple care needs. Each setting or organisation will deliver a specific service that will help an aspect of the service user's needs.

Gathering information about collaboration and teamwork during your sector engagement or your work experience placement

Whilst undertaking your sector engagement placement, you will need to identify and find examples of where **collaboration and teamwork** is demonstrated.

You could:

 ask the employer for a list of the different roles within the setting

 make a list of the different job roles that you have observed or worked alongside

 divide your list of team members into 'frontline care workers' and 'care and support functions'.

The role of professionalism in health and social care

Professionalism in the health and social care sector is expected by individuals receiving care and support. Professionalism can refer to duty of care, confidentiality and respecting individuals' rights.

Duty of care	Duty of care is a legal obligation for the care worker to provide high-quality care to the best of their ability, meeting the required standards. Workers should act within their own level of competence and not take on anything they cannot do safely.
Principles of care	Principles of care inform care workers daily in practice within health and social settings. These principles of care can help to provide high-quality care and support for the service users in Wales, and underpin the work of all care workers.
Confidentiality	Confidentiality is about keeping information private when it should be kept private. This includes written records, computer records and verbal information. A health and social care worker will know a great deal about the person they are looking after. It is therefore essential that the information is kept confidential, and not passed on without the individual's permission.
Respecting individuals' rights	All service users have rights, and these should be respected at all times by the care workers. This includes being treated fairly and not being discriminated against.
Caring skills	Caring skills are carried out by care workers constantly, and most will be carried out without the care worker knowing they are using them. For some care workers, these caring skills will come naturally, but some will need to be learned and practised – such as how to use effective communication techniques.

Gathering information about professionalism during your sector engagement or your work experience placement

Whilst undertaking your sector engagement placement, you will need to **identify** and **find examples** of where professionalism is demonstrated.

You could:

 ask the employer or the care workers what 'professionalism' means to them

 make a list of examples of professionalism you have observed.

Effective communication, co-production, collaboration, teamwork and professionalism supports:

A high standard of outcome-focused care and support

Successful and efficient teamwork

Better working environments for staff and individuals accessing care and support, including the co-production model

Improved experience for the individual's carers and families

A seamless service between all forms of outcome-focused care and support

Personal safety of individuals, and prevents errors occurring

Checklist for assignment

In preparation for your assignment, you must ensure that you have included all the details and the required information, and that you have included all of the examples from your setting/service.

Give an example of how you have witnessed each of the following characteristics as demonstrated during your sector engagement. These should include:

- effective communication
- co-production
- collaboration
- teamwork
- professionalism in the health and social care sector

CASE STUDY

Gavin lives with dementia and lives in a residential care home. Every morning, Gavin walks to the local newsagent to collect his newspaper. However, staff at the care home want to stop Gavin's morning visit to the newsagent, because once he has bought his newspaper, he often forgets to return to the care home. Unfortunately, there are insufficient staff at the care home to accompany Gavin to the shop, and Gavin prefers to go alone, since he feels it gives him more independence.

The three problems facing the care home management are:

1   Gavin's poor memory means they cannot trust him to get home safely from the newsagent.

2   Inadequate staffing levels to be able to support Gavin to go to the newsagent.

3   Staff attitudes – they believe it is easier and safer to stop Gavin going to the newsagent.

Gavin's social worker has met with Gavin and his carers at the care home, and produced a care plan. The outcome is that a risk assessment has been carried out and found that with a 'simple verbal reminder', Gavin could return to the care home safely after his visit to the newsagent.

■ The social worker, Gavin, the care home staff, and the owner of the newsagent agreed that the staff at the newsagent would talk to Gavin every morning when he bought his newspaper and remind him to return to the care home after leaving the shop.

■ Gavin was given a mobile phone so that care home staff could contact him if he did not return as expected.

Outcomes

■ Gavin's independence and empowerment have been maintained.

■ Co-production involved the service user Gavin, care home staff and the social worker in meetings.

■ Collaboration involved several groups working together.

■ Teamwork involved all those involved co-operating and working towards a common goal – which was Gavin's health and well-being. Gavin's dementia and loss of memory did not prevent him from doing activities he enjoys.

■ Professionalism by the health and social care workers showed competence in working collaboratively to secure a positive outcome for both Gavin and the care home staff.

Non-Examination Assessment – Task B

> **Choose three of the following and examine their importance in the work of health and social care setting/services. Give an example of how you have seen each of your chosen three demonstrated within your sector engagement:**
>
> - **Effective communication**
> - **Co-production**
> - **Collaboration**
> - **Teamwork**
> - **Professionalism in the health and social care sector.**

Answers must provide a detailed discussion focusing on a setting/ service directly experienced as part of sector engagement and include the importance of:

- Effective communication and its role in providing quality care and support to improve well-being outcomes for individuals. Care workers are expected to effectively communicate with individuals to determine their care and support needs and solve any problems in a proactive manner.

- Co-production is a way of thinking about how care and support services are designed, delivered, and evaluated. It involves working in equal partnership to make care and support services more effective, efficient, and sustainable.

- Collaboration is the basis of success in any team. When health and social care providers work in collaboration, patient outcomes and quality of care tend to improve.

- Teamwork in health and social care brings together professionals with different skills, abilities, and talents to provide the best possible care and treatment for individuals.

- Professionalism in the health and social care sector is expected by individuals receiving care and support. This is achieved by the shared competency standards and ethical values that are upheld by care workers.

What the examiner is looking for

1 A clear and detailed description of good practice in your work experience setting and in the sector.

2 The same emphasis of good practice applied to the three chosen elements.

3 A broad range of examples from the work experience setting or from the health and social care sector.

4   An explanation of the purpose of the examples of good practice chosen. Remember to do so within the context of effective communication, co-production, collaboration, teamwork and/or professionalism. Remember also that you will need to refer specifically to your work experience placement or your experience in the sector you have chosen.

Reading and further research

Community care

https://chcymru.org.uk/?

https://www.gov.wales/8-million-community-care-support-people-stay-well-home-and-reduce-pressure-hospitals

Ideas that change health and care

www.kingsfund.org.uk

Communication skills in health and social care by Bernard Moss (9781526490155)

Health Education and Improvement Wales

https://www.gov.wales/health-education-and-improvement-wales

https://heiw.nhs.wales/

Skills for Health

www.skillsforhealth.org.uk

Social Care Institute for Excellence

www.scie.org.uk

Co-production

https://socialcare.wales/resources-guidance/information-and-learning-hub/learning-resources/social-services-and-well-being-wales-act-2014/principles-of-the-act/co-production#:

The Health Foundation

https://www.health.org.uk/

Public Health Wales

https://phw.nhs.wales/services-and-teams/nhs-wales-health-collaborative/

The Nursing & Midwifery Council

https://www.nmc.org.uk/

Professionalism by Alan Cribb and Sharon Gewitz (9780745653174)

Health and Care Quality Professional Standards

https://www.gov.wales/health-and-care-quality-standards-2023-whc2023013

6.3: How codes of conduct and practice are adhered to and applied in health and social care settings

This chapter looks at codes of conduct and practice and how they are used and applied in health and social care settings. You will use the information in this chapter and the research gathered from your sector engagement and/or work experience to produce your assignment.

What are codes of conduct and professional practice?

Codes of conduct and practice in health and social care settings set out the standards that all care workers will be expected to follow. Codes of contact and practice have been designed to ensure that high-quality care is being delivered to at least the minimum standards set out in the codes. In most health and social care settings, the codes of conduct are included in the staff handbook, or within the policies and procedures folder.

Key terms

Codes of conduct and practice
Documents that outline the standards that care workers are expected to follow when working. They will aim to ensure that high-quality care is conducted to a minimum standard.

Policies
A policy will tell the care worker how they should perform specific duties in the care setting.

Procedures
A procedure will set out the way in which a care worker will need to deal with a specific issue. It will set out in detail the steps to follow.

Codes of conduct and professional practice include, for example:

Code of Professional Practice for Social Care

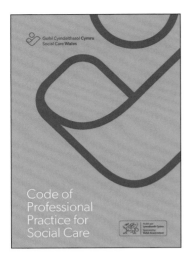

The **Code of Professional Practice for Social Care** provides rules or standards that describe the conduct and practice required of social workers and employers in Wales. The Code is a list of statements that describe the standards of professional conduct and practice required of those employed in the social care professions in Wales. It plays a key part in raising awareness of the standards of conduct and practice that are expected of the profession. The Code of Professional Practice for Social Care includes detailed practical guidance on how to comply with legal obligations for matters such as:

- Care workers helping service users to understand their rights.
- Care workers focusing on gaining service user trust and respect.
- Care workers helping service users to speak up on any issue of concern (related to an individual's physical, psychological, emotional, and spiritual well-being).
- Care workers should respect each individual and help to keep them safe.
- Care workers should ensure that service users can trust them to do an excellent job.
- Care workers ensure that service users receive support following their own professional training for their role.

The residential child care worker

The residential child care worker codes of conduct are for residential child care workers registered with Social Care Wales.

The codes set out how residential child care workers need to undertake their roles in a professional way. Residential child care workers undertake a professional role, providing care and support for children and young people who require care away from their families for short or extended periods. Residential child care workers have a responsibility for:

- Safeguarding.
- Promoting the rights and well-being of children and young people.
- Providing care and support.

https://socialcare.wales/resources-guidance/improving-care-and-support/children-who-are-looked-after/residential-child-care-worker-resource

Health and Care Professions Council (HCPC)

The standards of the **Health and Care Professions Council** protect the service users by regulating health and care professionals. They achieve this by setting mandatory standards for care workers.

The aims and objectives of these mandatory standards include:

1 To promote and protect the interests of service users and carers.

2 To communicate appropriately and effectively.

3 To work within the parameters of the knowledge and skills of practitioners.

4 Delegate appropriately.

5 Respect confidentiality.

6 Manage risk.

7 Report concerns about safety.

8 Be open and transparent when things go wrong.

9 Be honest and trustworthy.

10 Keep comprehensive records of your work.

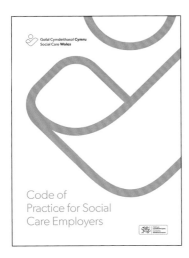

Code of Practice for Social Care Employers

The **Code of Practice for Social Care Employers** (the employers' Code) is published by Social Care Wales under Section 112 of the Regulation and Inspection of Social Care (Wales) Act 2016 (the Act). It is a list of statements describing the standards expected of social care employers.

Section 1   Make sure that those seeking to enter the social care workforce are suitable and that they understand their roles and responsibilities.

Section 2   The requirement that policies, systems and practices are in place to enable social care workers to meet their Code of Professional Practice for Social Care.

Section 3   Provide and support, learning and development opportunities to enable social care workers to develop and enrich their knowledge and skills.

Section 4   Have policies and systems to protect people from damaging or dangerous situations, behaviour, and practice.

Section 5   Promote the Code of Professional Practice for Social Care and co-operate with the procedures of Social Care Wales.

To ensure that workers in Wales provide excellent care and support to individuals, the **Social Care Professional Code of Practice** (the Code) also includes a requirement that carers have to register with Social Care Wales. All carers must register before they can work in the social care sector in Wales. The main purpose of the Code and the registration requirement is to provide the best care and support within a safeguarding framework for the patients or clients.

Registered social care workers and social care managers must follow the Code of Professional Practice to continue working in social care. The list of employees who must register with Social Care Wales and comply with the requirements of the Code includes social care workers, social work students and social work managers. Social care workers, social work students and social care managers who must register with them include:

- adult care home workers and managers
- domiciliary care workers and domiciliary care managers
- residential child care workers and residential child care managers
- residential family centre workers and managers
- social care workers and social work students
- adoption service managers
- adult placement managers

- advocacy managers working with children and young people
- fostering service managers
- special school residential managers

It is a legal requirement that social workers and social care managers must register once they have completed their qualification, or when they start their new job. Social care workers have six months from the start date of their role to register with Social Care Wales. It is a legal requirement to register with Social Care Wales.

Code of Conduct for Healthcare Support Workers in Wales

The **Code of Conduct for Healthcare Support Workers in Wales** focuses on making sure that service users and the public receive a consistent, high-quality, safe, and effective service from healthcare support workers.

Healthcare support workers must:

1 Be accountable by making sure they can always answer for their actions or omissions.

2 Promote and uphold the privacy, dignity, rights and well-being of service users and their carers at all times.

3 Work in collaboration with their colleagues, as part of a team, to ensure the delivery of high-quality safe care to service users and their families.

4 Communicate in an open, transparent, and effective way to promote the well-being of service users and carers.

5 Respect a person's right to confidentiality, protecting and upholding their privacy.

6 Improve the quality of care to service users by updating their knowledge, skills, and experience through personal and professional development.

7 To promote equality, all service users, colleagues and members of the public are entitled to be treated fairly and without bias.

Code of Practice for NHS Wales Employers

The **Code of Practice for NHS Wales Employers** is an important assurance mechanism, supporting the employment of healthcare support workers in Wales. The Code of Practice for Employers is supported by a Code of Conduct for Healthcare Support Workers, which describes the standards individuals must comply with. Employers should be familiar with the Code of Conduct and ensure staff are supported to achieve the designated standards.

To meet their responsibilities in relation to supporting healthcare support workers to comply with their Code of Conduct, **employers must**:

1   Make sure that people are suitable to be employed within the healthcare workforce, and that they understand their roles, accountabilities, and responsibilities.

2   Have procedures in place so that healthcare support workers can meet the requirements of the Code of Conduct.

3   Provide timely, appropriate, and accessible education, training, and development opportunities to enable healthcare support workers to develop and strengthen their skills and knowledge.

4   Promote this Code of Practice and the Code of Conduct for Healthcare Support Workers to staff, service users and other stakeholders, and ensure its use in day-to-day practice within your organisation.

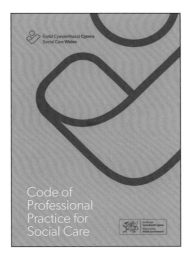

Code of Professional Practice for Social Care

This code provides practical guidance for social care workers registered with Social Care Wales. It builds on the Code of Professional Practice for Social Care and aims to:

■ describe what is expected of social workers

■ support social care workers to deliver a good service

The guidance covers the following:

■ Person-centred social work.

■ Good social work practice.

■ Safeguarding individuals.

■ Developing and managing self.

■ Collaborating with colleagues.

■ Contributing to service improvement.

■ Good conduct.

How are codes of practice and guidance applied by employees in practice?

- ■ **Embed excellent communication between staff**

- ■ **Training to ensure that team members are able to implement the codes of practice and guidance**

- ■ **Mechanism for staff development**

- ■ **Supervision and performance management**

- ■ **Complaint and compliment services**

- ■ **Registration and workforce regulation – fitness to practise, investigations, and proceedings**

- ■ **Regulation and inspection services to monitor implementation of the codes of practice and conduct**

Gofal Cymdeithasol **Cymru**
Social Care **Wales**

Registration with Social Care Wales

To make sure that workers in Wales provide individuals with excellent care and support them, the **Code of Professional Practice for Social Care** provides the mandatory standards for social care workers. These standards for care professionals provide a quality framework to help keep patients and clients safe and well. An additional feature of embedding excellent care and protecting the public is to ensure that only those who are competent and qualified can deliver care and support. Therefore, **social care workers need to be registered** with Social Care Wales before practising. Healthcare workers have to register before they practise, confirming that they are qualified to work in a social care setting. By being registered, care workers can show that they are part of a professional workforce, and that they have the knowledge and the skills that are crucial to providing diligent care and support to the people of Wales. Social care workers who are registered must follow the Code of Professional Practice to work in the social care sector.

Social workers and social work students will need to register with Social Care Wales.

Workers included for registration in social care includes:

- adult care home workers
- residential child care workers (including secure children's accommodation)
- residential family centre workers.

Social care managers will need to register with Social Care Wales. Social care managers that need to register include:

- adoption service managers
- adult care home managers
- adult placement managers
- advocacy managers (services for children and young people)
- domiciliary care managers
- fostering service managers
- residential child care managers (including secure children's accommodation)
- residential family centre managers
- special school residential managers.

All social workers and social care managers must register once they have completed their qualification, or when they start in their post.

All social care workers have six months from the start date of their role to register with Social Care Wales. It is a legal requirement for workers in these roles to register with Social Care Wales.

Gathering information about codes of conduct and practice followed by employees during your engagement with the sector or during your work experience placement

Whilst undertaking your sector engagement placement, you will need to identify the codes of conduct and practice that all employees in the setting should adhere to.

You could:

 ask the employer for a copy of the staff handbook

 make a list of the different codes of conduct and practice policies that they follow

 interview other care workers to find out the impact of codes of conduct and practice on them being able to deliver high-quality care.

What is the purpose of professional bodies?

Professional bodies are organisations whose individual members practise a profession or occupation; the organisation maintains an oversight of the knowledge, skills, conduct and practice of that profession or occupation.

Professional body/regulatory body	An organisation that sets standards, and rules for a specific profession. They maintain a register of qualified care workers, and have powers to remove those who are unfit to practise.

All care workers in health and social care settings in Wales will need to be registered with a professional body. Professional bodies provide an enrolment process, guidance, support, and a regulatory framework for care workers and their settings.

The aims and objectives of professional bodies include the following:

- Promoting professional standards of practice and ethics
- Providing information and advice
- Protecting and supporting workers
- Providing opportunities for their members to network
- Publishing professional journals
- Providing career development in the profession.

Professional bodies in health and social care include:

British Medical Association (BMA)

The **British Medical Association (BMA)** is the trade union and professional body for doctors in the UK.

> 'We are committed to promoting equal rights and opportunities, supporting diversity, and creating an open and inclusive environment for our members, employees, and stakeholders.
>
> We support our members in their professional lives, advocate for fairness and equality in the medical profession, and negotiate for better pay and working conditions.'

Royal College of Nursing Wales

The **Royal College of Nursing (RCN)** is the world's largest union and professional body for nursing staff.

> 'We are a membership organisation of over 465,000 registered nurses, midwives, health care assistants and nursing students.

As a member-led organisation, we work collaboratively with our members to:

- *influence governments and other bodies*
- *improve working conditions*
- *campaign on issues to raise the profile of the nursing community.'*

The **Royal College of Nursing Wales** represents nurses, health care assistants, nursing students and midwives across Wales.

British Association of Social Workers (BASW) and BASW Cymru

The **British Association of Social Workers (BASW)** is the UK's professional membership organisation for social work.

> *'We are the independent voice of social work. We champion social work and help members achieve the highest professional standards.'*

BASW Cymru represents all areas of social work, social workers, and students across Wales.

Nursing and Midwifery Council (NMC)

The Nursing and Midwifery Council is the independent regulator for nurses and midwives in the United Kingdom (UK). The core role of the NMC is to regulate and promote a high standard of knowledge and skills in order to embed professional standards for nurses and midwives. The organisation registers professionals who are eligible to practise and investigates concerns about nurses, midwives and nursing associates, and acts if required. It also supports the professions and the public by preparing resources and guidance to help them deliver the standards, and to address current issues or challenges.

The benefits of belonging to professional bodies for health and social care professionals include:

- Promoting professional standards of practice and ethics.
- Providing information and advice.
- Protecting and supporting workers.
- Providing opportunities for members to network.
- Publishing professional journals (members can read about, and refer to, issues raised).
- Providing career development opportunities.

Gathering information about job roles and their regulatory bodies codes of practice during your engagement with the sector, or during your work experience placement

Once you have collected the information about the care workers and who works within your setting, you will now need to find out which regulatory body they need to be registered with.

You could:

 ask the health and social care worker with which regulatory body are they registered

 research online who regulates that specific role.

What are trade unions?

Alongside regulatory bodies, many care workers within health and social care will also be a member of a trade union. A trade union consists of a group of people specialising in a particular profession or job, and offers advice and support to healthcare workers, in addition to improving the environment and the conditions of the job. The overarching aim of a trade union is to protect or improve working conditions and the working environment for its members. Trade unions can provide information, legal support, and advice to their members. They aim to protect and improve employees' pay and conditions of employment.

▲ **Nurses pay dispute in Cardiff**

Gathering information about job roles and their membership of a trade union during your engagement in the sector or during your work experience placement

Whilst undertaking your sector engagement placement, you will need to identify the job roles within the setting or the service and find out which trade unions they are members of.

You could:

 interview someone in the job role and find out which trade union they are a member of, finding out the benefits for the member

 research online the different trade unions and what benefits they provide to their members.

Ethics: these are the moral principles underpinning how a worker should act or behave.

Networking: this is an exchange of information or ideas with other workers from the same profession, usually in a more informal and social setting.

Complaints services: these deal with problems that service users want to resolve.

Compliment services: for service users, families, and carers to provide positive feedback if their experience of the service provision has merited praise.

Fitness to practise investigation: Fitness to practise is not only about professional performance; it also includes acts by the social worker that could damage the confidence of the public in the profession. Fitness to practise follows a

complaint about a worker who may have:

- made serious and /or repeated mistakes or omissions in care.
- failed to conduct appropriate and/or sufficient safeguarding assessments.
- failed to respond effectively to an individual's needs.
- failed to manage health conditions or care effectively, and may have caused an individual to be at risk.

Checklist for the assignment

In preparation for your assignment, you must ensure that you have sourced information about your setting or service to enable you to:

 analyse how codes of professional conduct and practice are used in practice and applied within the health and social care sector.

 use examples from your sector engagement to illustrate your answer.

Non-Examination Assessment – Task D

Analyse how codes of professional conduct and practice are adhered to and applied within the health and social care sector. Use examples from your sector engagement to illustrate your answer.

Answers must analyse a setting, or a service directly experienced as part of your sector engagement, and could include:

- the communication methods that are used to communicate with all of the staff
- offering training to ensure the code is understood
- practice and promotion by management
- supervision and performance management opportunities
- complaints and compliments services
- registration and workforce regulation: fitness to practise investigations and proceedings
- regulation and inspection services in inspecting codes of professional conduct/practice.

Reading and further research

Health and Care Quality Standards
https://www.gov.wales/health-and-care-quality-standards-2023-whc2023013

Code of Practice for Social Care Employers
https://socialcare.wales/cms-assets/documents/Employers-code.pdf

Code of Conduct for Healthcare Support Workers in Wales
cavuhb.nhs.wales/files/induction/code-of-conduct-1-pdf/

The Code of Practice for NHS Wales Employers
heiw.nhs.wales/files/weds-education-contracting-links/code-of-practice-for-nhs-wales-employers/

NHS Confederation in Wales – Welsh NHS Confederation
https://www.nhsconfed.org/wales

Social Care Wales – Registration
https://socialcare.wales/registration/why-we-register

Nursing and Midwifery Council
https://www.nmc.org.uk/about-us/our-role/

Royal College of Nursing Wales
https://www.rcn.org.uk/wales

British Medical Association (Wales) (BMA)
https://www.bma.org.uk/

BASW Cymru
https://new.basw.co.uk/about-basw/social-work-around-uk/basw-cymru

6.4: Role of employers in promoting and protecting the rights of the employee

This chapter will be looking at the role of employers in protecting the rights of the employee. You will use the information in this chapter and the research gathered from your sector engagement or work experience to prepare your assignment.

How should employers promote and protect the rights of employees working within the health and social care setting?

Employers within health and social care settings in Wales have a responsibility to promote and protect the rights of the employees working within their setting. They will need to know the standards set in legislation and how these standards are included in practice by the implementation of policies, procedures, and strategies.

Rights of employees

The rights of employees include the following rights:

- Salary
- Hours of work and overtime
- Working patterns
- Pension
- Holiday leave
- Sick leave
- Job security and satisfaction

Basic employment rights

All employers must ensure that they are aware of, and respond to, basic employment rights such as pay, sick leave, holiday leave and the rights of part-time staff.

Salary

Salaries for care workers are usually based on where their skills and abilities place them on a pay scale, specifically for their job role. However, some will have an hourly pay that will be decided by the health and social care setting.

National Minimum Wage	The National Minimum Wage (for those of at least school leaving age). The rates change on 1 April every year.
National Living Wage	These rates are for the National Living Wage (for those aged 23 and over). The rates change on 1 April every year.

Details of rates for the National Minimum Wage and the National Living Wage are available on the Gov UK website.

https://www.gov.uk/national-minimum-wage-rates

Sick leave and holiday leave

Sick leave	If staff are too ill to work, they are entitled to Statutory Sick Pay (SSP), which is paid by employers for a defined period. For the latest information on the current rates:
	https://www.gov.uk/statutory-sick-pay
	If the employer has its own Sick Pay Scheme, then staff may be entitled to more than the SSP payment. To qualify for SSP, a staff member must earn an average wage that is above a certain amount.
Holiday Leave	Almost all workers are legally entitled to 5.6 weeks' (about 28 days') paid annual leave a year (known as the Statutory Leave Entitlement). An employer can include bank holidays as part of the statutory leave entitlement.
Part-time worker's rights	Part-time workers are protected from being treated less favourably than equivalent full-time workers just because they are part-time.
	A part-time worker is someone who works fewer hours than a full-time worker. There is no specific number of hours that makes someone full- or part-time, but a full-time worker will usually work 35 hours or more a week.

Discrimination issues

Employers in health and social care services must understand how to identify and challenge discrimination and harassment within the setting.

Protected characteristics include:

Age, Disability, Marriage or Civil partnership, Pregnancy or Maternity, Race, Religion and belief, Sex, Gender reassignment and Sexual orientation.

The Equality Act 2010 replaced the existing anti-discrimination laws with a single Act. It simplified the law, removing inconsistencies and making it easier for people to understand and comply with it. The Act also strengthened the law in important ways to help tackle discrimination and inequality. A summary guide tells you how the Equality Act 2010 changes how individuals have to act in order to prevent and address discrimination when providing goods, facilities, and services to the public, for example as a residential care home, community shop or after-school club. These parts of the Act came into effect on 1 October 2010.

https://www.gov.uk/guidance/equality-act-2010-guidance

The **Safety, Health and Welfare at Work Act 2005**, which repealed and replaced the Safety, Health and Welfare at Work Act 1989, was brought in to make further provision for the safety, health and welfare of people at work. This Act clarified and enhanced the responsibilities of the employer, self-employed people, employees and various other parties in relation to safety, health and welfare at work.

Safety, Health and Welfare at Work Act 2005

Employers of health and social care settings need to ensure the health and safety of their employees and the service users. They need to know the basic principles of the **Safety, Health and Welfare at Work Act 2005**. The Act covers:

- General duties of employers
- Information to employees
- Instruction, training and supervision of employees
- Emergencies and serious and imminent dangers
- Protective and preventive measures
- Hazard identification and risk assessment
- Safety statement
- Co-operation
- Health surveillance and medical fitness to work
- Safety representative
- Employee consultation
- Penalisation

General duties of the employer include, for example:

- Accidents in the workplace
- Reporting of injuries in the workplace
- Food safety and hygiene
- First aid
- Risk assessments
- Preventing infection
- Personal protective equipment
- Fire safety
- Emergency procedures
- Controls of substances hazardous to health

Policies, procedures, initiatives, and strategies

Employers from health and social care settings need to know about the policies, procedures, initiatives, and the necessary strategies required to help protect the rights of their employees. In particular, they need to be aware of those that affect their employees' health and well-being, including confidentiality and social media policies.

Good practice within health and social care settings in Wales will:

- provide support to all care workers within the care setting
- develop policies that provide 'high-quality care'
- promote equality and anti-discriminatory practice
- provide training and development opportunities for all care workers
- produce detailed procedures to achieve best practice

The Well-being of Future Generations (Wales) Act 2015 is about **improving the social, economic, environmental, and cultural well-being of Wales**. It makes the public bodies listed in the Act focus more on the long term, working better with people and communities and each other, looking to prevent problems and taking a more seamless approach.

Well-being goals

A Globally Responsible Wales

A Prosperous Wales

A Resilient Wales

A Wales of Vibrant Culture and Thriving Welsh Language

A Healthier Wales

A Wales of Cohesive Communities

A More Equal Wales

Collaboration	Integration	Involvement	Long-term	Prevention

Acting in collaboration with any other person (or different parts of the body itself) that could help the body to meet its well-being objectives.	Considering how the public body's well-being objectives may impact upon each of the well-being goals, on their other objectives, or on the objectives of other public bodies.	The importance of involving people with an interest in achieving the well-being goals, and ensuring that those people reflect the diversity of the area which the body serves.	The importance of balancing short-term needs with the need to safeguard the long-term needs.	How acting to prevent problems occurring or getting worse may help public bodies meet their objectives.

General Data Protection Regulation (GDPR) and The Data Protection Act 2018

The **General Data Protection Regulation (GDPR)** is a European Union regulation on information privacy in the European Union and the European Economic Area. The GDPR is an important component of EU privacy law and human rights law, in particular Article 8 of the Charter of Fundamental Rights of the European Union. Since Brexit, GDPR is retained in domestic law as the 'UK GDPR', but the UK has the independence to keep the framework under review. The 'UK GDPR' sits alongside an amended version of the **Data Protection Act 2018**. The Data Protection Act is the UK's implementation of the General Protection Regulation (GDPR). The Data Protection Act 2018 controls how your personal information is used by organisations, businesses, or the government. Healthcare organisations that use personal data must follow strict rules to make sure that information complies with the Data Protection Act 2018. This Act sets out clear guidance that all individuals have the right to:

- be informed about how your data is being used
- receive clear information about what settings will do with the data provided by the user
- access their own personal information
- request that their data be revised if out of date, or to be erased
- request information about the reasoning behind any automated decisions
- prevent or query the automated processing of their personal data.

There is stronger legal protection for more sensitive information such as, for example, health, race, ethnic background, religious beliefs, and sexual orientation.

What duty of care do organisations have towards their employees' health and well-being?

All health and social care settings in Wales have a duty of care towards their employees, particularly for their health and well-being. Working within health and social care in Wales should be a rewarding and enjoyable experience for all care workers. Care workers should feel safe and supported whilst carrying out their job role. One way in which they do this is by the employer building a **supportive culture** which is **holistic** and **comprehensive**. Another way is by **tackling the stigma** about accessing support services.

A supportive culture in health and social care settings is based on establishing good working relationships

Good working relationships focus on:	Good working relationships lead to staff having:
Honesty	A clear sense of identity
Trust	Higher self-esteem
Support	Self-worth
Respect	The development of new skills
Good communication	Positive self-image
Reliability	

Gathering information about the rights of the employees during your engagement with the sector or during your work experience placement

During your sector engagement placement, you will need to obtain the following information about the **rights of the employees** within your setting.

You could:

 ask the employees about their rights within the setting/service and their knowledge of policies, procedures, initiatives affecting their health and well-being at work.

 actively seek information relating to basic employment rights for workers in the setting or sector. This research task may include, for example, rights in terms of rates of pay, minimum wage, living wage, absence arrangements and sick pay, holiday arrangements and holiday pay and part-time worker rights.

Checklist for assignment

When you prepare your assignment, it is absolutely essential that you gather the information required for the assignment within the setting itself or within the service itself. The main purpose of this is to:

 prepare a detailed survey of the various arrangements, duties and responsibilities of employees and employers in relation to that specific location or that specific service.

 outline the role of the employer in promoting and protecting the rights of employees who work in the setting or who offer a specific service.

Non-Examination Assessment – Task A(i)

> **The Non-Examination Task A(i) INTRODUCTION**
>
> **Write an introduction about the setting/service**
>
> - **The main purpose of the chosen setting/service**
> - **The role of the employer in promoting and protecting the rights of employees working in the setting/service.**

Your response could include reference to the following ways that an employer promotes and protects the rights of employees working in your placement setting/service by:

- Anti-discrimination and anti-harassment practices.

- Promoting equality.

- Health and safety principles.

- Embedding and implementing policies and procedures.

- Strategies and arrangements to deal with sensitive and personal issues. For example, tackling the stigma around accessing support services for mental ill health.

- Arrangements for ensuring confidentiality and social media policies.

- Legislation: Well-being of Future Generations Act 2015, Data Protection Act 2018.

- Duty of care with a focus on health and well-being.

- Holistic, comprehensive, and supportive culture.

What the examiner is looking for

1   It is extremely important that you focus on **the role of the employer** in providing adequate information on the rights of the employees who work in the setting or within the health and social care service, and that those rights are fully implemented and enforced.

2   That you **exemplify the evidence of action and promotion based on your experience** in the setting or within the service. Your research into the role of the employer on promoting and protecting the rights of employees will enable you to see if the setting or service reflects the legislative and regulatory requirements.

3   You need to **investigate in detail the role of the employer** in promoting and protecting employees' rights to find out if the setting or service is implementing policies and procedures to prevent discrimination and bullying, and whether they are providing a safe working environment. Does the setting or service understand and comply with anti-discrimination laws, and does it recognise the benefits of an inclusive and diverse workforce? Do they undertake risk assessments and act based on findings? Are they regularly reviewing policies and decisions to ensure equality? Are they encouraging a culture of equality and fairness, and setting clear guidelines for equality and disciplinary procedures?

Reading and further research

Employment status and employment rights
https://www.gov.uk/government/publications/employment-status-and-employment-rights/employment-status-and-employment-rights-guidance-for-hr-professionals-legal-professionals-and-other-groups

HSE: Information about health and safety at work
https://www.hse.gov.uk/pubns/law.pdf

Equality Act 2010 – Guidance
https://www.gov.uk/guidance/equality-act-2010-guidance

6.5: Safeguarding in practice

We have already had an introduction to safeguarding in Unit 5. This chapter will provide you with more detail and a greater understanding when applying safeguarding in practice within health and social care settings. We will investigate what happens if safeguarding is breached, and the potential risks that may follow. You will use the information in this chapter, in addition to your research gathered during your sector engagement and work experience. This information will form the basis of your assignment.

In practice, how is safeguarding achieved within different settings?

In all health and social care settings in Wales, care workers will come into contact with children and adults who may be at risk of abuse and neglect. All health and social care settings should have a safeguarding policy, with specific procedures to follow. Safeguarding procedures ensure that the children or adults using those services are protected from abuse and neglect through placing safeguarding at the centre of all practice.

Safeguarding procedures in health and care settings aim to ensure that all care workers understand what is meant by safeguarding, their roles, and their colleagues' roles and responsibilities in ensuring that safeguarding processes are followed.

Forms of abuse and neglect

Physical abuse	When an individual is physically hit, kicked, slapped, scalded, or treated in a rough manner.
Sexual abuse	When an individual is touched inappropriately or forced to take part in sexual activity.
Emotional and psychological abuse	When an individual is being called names, shouted at, or manipulated.
Financial abuse	When an individual has their money stolen or it is being withheld from them.
Neglect	When an individual is denied sufficient care.

Individuals and groups that are more likely to experience abuse include:

- Children
- Older adults
- Individuals living with disabilities
- Individuals living with learning difficulties
- Individuals living with mental illness.

Values-based recruitment (VBR)

Values-based recruitment (VBR)	Is an approach to recruitment which helps an organisation find and employ people with the same personal values as their staff. Values-based recruitment (VBR) is an approach which (including aptitude and skills) attracts and selects employees and trainees on the basis that their individual values and behaviours align with the values of the NHS Constitution.

Employers will also focus on implementing safeguarding procedures and practice in place through the use of:

- Values-based recruitment (VBR).
- Implementing induction sessions at the outset for staff.
- Establish regular updating sessions to review processes and procedures.

Key terms

Safeguarding
Safeguarding means preventing and protecting children and adults at risk from abuse or neglect and educating those around them to recognise the signs and dangers.

Designated Safeguarding Person
The identified person within the organisation who is available to discuss safeguarding concerns.

Disclosure and Barring Service (DBS)

The **Disclosure and Barring Service (DBS)** helps employers in England, Wales and Northern Ireland make safer recruitment decisions, and prevents unsuitable people from working with vulnerable groups, including children. The DBS decides whether it is suitable for a person to be placed on, or removed from, a list of people barred from working in certain occupations within health and social care and other settings.

Safeguarding Boards

The **National Independent Safeguarding Board Wales** advises the Welsh Government and works with the safeguarding boards to protect children and adults from harm in health and social care settings. The National Independent Safeguarding Board Wales was set up under the Social Services and Well-being (Wales) Act 2014. The National Independent Safeguarding Board works in collaboration with the six multi-agency strategic boards of relevant partner agencies set up across Wales. These are designed to protect children and adults at risk of abuse or neglect and to prevent those children and adults from becoming at risk of abuse or neglect.

- Cardiff and Vale Regional Safeguarding Board
- Cysur/Mid & West Wales Safeguarding Board
- Cwm Taf Morgannwg Safeguarding Board
- Gwent Safeguarding Board
- North Wales Safeguarding Board
- West Glamorgan Safeguarding Board

Find Your Regional Board – Safeguarding Board Wales
https://safeguardingboard.wales/find-your-board/

If a care worker becomes aware or believes that an individual is in immediate danger, they must contact the police straight away. All health and social settings must have safeguarding policies and procedures in place which explain exactly what needs to happen if a care worker believes an individual to be in danger.

Whistleblowing policy

Whistleblowing is the term applied to a situation where a care worker raises a concern or concerns to individuals who have the power, and presumed willingness to take corrective action. It is a way to bring attention to an issue or concern happening within the health and social care setting. Whistleblowing is an essential part of the safeguarding procedure, and all care workers have a duty to report any concerns that could potentially put an individual in a situation where they could be abused or harmed.

Breaching safeguarding procedures and policies

If safeguarding procedures and policies are breached, this could lead to:

- Abuse and neglect for the individuals accessing care and support.

- Legal action (civil or criminal prosecution) against the individual who is in breach and/or the organisation/care setting.

- Disciplinary action against the staff involved in 'wrongdoing'.

- Dismissal for a member of staff who has breached safeguarding procedures.

- Loss of trust of the service users in the setting and care workers.

- Negative publicity for the health and social care setting, damaging the health and social care setting's reputation.

- Failure to attract and employ new care workers.

Feedback from individuals of several health and social care settings is used to assist the Welsh Government in preparing policies and procedures for the sector. This evidence will be collected from several sources, including hospitals and care homes. The feedback received will be used to develop Welsh Government policies, procedures, and guidelines. An example of such a document is 'A Healthier Wales: a long-term plan for health and social care'.

https://www.gov.wales/healthier-wales-long-term-plan-health-and-social-care

Gathering information about safeguarding policies and procedures during your work experience or service placement

Whilst undertaking your sector engagement placement, you will need to identify the **safeguarding policies and procedures** during your work experience placement.

You could:

 ask the employer or senior staff the name of their designated safeguarding person/s

 ask for the safeguarding policy for the health and social care setting and ask about how regularly reviewing and updating of processes and procedures takes place

 observe the safeguarding procedures in practice at the health and social care setting

Checklist for the assignment

In preparation for your assignment, you must ensure that you have sourced the relevant information from your setting or service to enable you to:

 explain how safeguarding is achieved within the setting or service to ensure that individuals accessing outcome-focused, person-centred care and support can live free from harm, abuse, and neglect.

 outline the potential outcomes if the setting or service's safeguarding policies and procedures are not followed, and the role of an effective complaints system and employee duty to report through 'whistleblowing'.

Non-Examination Assessment – Task C(i)

The Non-Examination Assessment - Section C Task C(i)
Explain how safeguarding is achieved within the setting/service to ensure that individuals accessing outcome-focused, person-centred care and support can live free from harm, abuse, and neglect.

The Non-Examination Assessment - Section C Task C(ii)
Outline the potential outcomes if the setting/service's safeguarding policies and procedures are not followed.

The Non-Examination Assessment – Section C Task C(i):

Answers must provide an explanation of how safeguarding is achieved within the setting or service. You must also make specific reference to how safeguarding is achieved in the setting or service as directly experienced by you as part of sector engagement. You should include reference to how the setting or the service provides a person-centred approach that should ensure that individuals receive personal care and support and that they are kept safe from harm, abuse, and neglect. During your placement, you will need to focus on how this is being achieved in the setting or the service:

- Does the setting placement provide a person-centred approach which will empower people to take charge of their own health and health care?

- Does the setting placement place an emphasis on getting the views of patients that can help to improve the health of the patient. A person-centred approach will focus on the needs of the patient to ensure that they are always treated with dignity, respect, and compassion. This could also include the input of relatives.

- Is safeguarding at the centre of the care workers' routine and practice at the placement?

- Does the placement provide an induction course, and do they provide ongoing training of all staff? Do they to ensure that all staff members are fully aware of current legislation, standards, policies, and procedures?

- Does the setting or service record accurate and keep up to date records in relation to safeguarding?

- What is the staff ratio in relation to staff numbers and patients or clients?

- Have they embedded an effective and accessible complaints procedure?

- Are they promoting a person-centred approach and promoting well-being in all of their safeguarding arrangements?

■ How do they ensure that the safeguarding policies and procedures are regularly reviewed, and that processes and procedures are being updated accordingly?

■ Are the services provided by the Disclosure and Barring Service (DBS) used to check staff backgrounds?

■ Does the feedback from individuals in the setting or service influence Welsh Government policies?

■ Describe how the duty to report policies ('whistleblowing') is implemented within the setting or service.

■ How does the setting or service ensure that they are not in breach of contract and that they can avoid prosecution?

The Non-Examination Assessment Section C Task C(ii):

Your answer must examine and define what are the potential outcomes if the safeguarding policies and procedures at the setting or service are not followed. You will need to consider the outcomes for both the individuals themselves and the setting. Your answer must be based on your actual experiences at the setting as part of your sector engagement. You will need to gather information at the setting to illustrate the potential outcomes for the individuals if the safeguarding policies and procedures have not been followed. These negative outcomes could include:

■ **Vulnerability**: the individual accessing care and support through the service or setting may be at a greater risk of being vulnerable to harm, abuse and neglect.

■ **Unexpected or unintended harm and risk to individuals**: the needs of an individual accessing care and support at the setting or service may be compromised if the healthcare and safeguarding policies and procedures are not followed in full. If the setting fails to comply with safeguarding policies, then individuals are not protected from physical, emotional, and sexual abuse, neglect, or harm.

■ **Legal consequences and prosecution**: the setting or service, staff and individuals may be subject to disciplinary action if the health and social care worker or the placement setting breaches policies and procedures. These policies and procedures are monitored by Public Health Wales (PHW) who have mechanisms in place to identify and report abuse, harm, or neglect within a setting. Failure to comply will result in legal challenges and consequences. The setting or service providing care may also be subject to prosecution if these safeguarding protocols have not been followed by the setting.

■ **Reputation**: Not following safeguarding policies can lead to damaging the reputation of the setting or service. This could lead to healthcare providers losing the confidence of the individuals and the public.

What is the examiner is looking for

Assessment task C(i):

1 To reach the higher mark bands, you should provide examples from your placement to support the safeguarding information within your answer.

2 All vital components of safeguarding policies and procedures must be included in your answer.

3 You will need to provide evidence to illustrate how safeguarding policies and practices within the setting ensure that individuals are being safeguarded. Illustrate your answer with examples of good practice and how the setting provides care and support by adopting person-centred approaches.

4 Give examples of why safeguarding policies and procedures are essential for ensuring the safety and well-being of vulnerable individuals. Show how these policies and procedures provide a framework for identifying, preventing, and responding to risks within the placement setting.

Assessment task C(ii):

1 You must provide detailed information about all of the internal safeguarding processes of policy and procedures within the placement organisation.

2 You need to show that not adhering to safeguarding policies in a healthcare setting can have serious consequences for patients and vulnerable individuals. Here are some potential outcomes you need to consider carefully:

- **Risk to patients' safety and well-being**: When safeguarding procedures are not followed, patients or clients may be exposed to harm, abuse, or neglect. Failure to protect their health and human rights can lead to adverse physical, emotional, or psychological outcomes.

- **Missed opportunities for intervention**: Poor information-sharing and failure to identify safeguarding risks can result in missed opportunities to intervene. In serious cases, this can lead to inadequate care and negative outcomes for patients and clients.

- **Legal and regulatory consequences**: Healthcare providers and organisations that neglect safeguarding responsibilities may face legal action. Regulatory bodies such as Care Inspectorate Wales (CIW) monitor compliance, and failure to improve or respond to recommendations can have serious consequences.

- **Resource issues**: Inadequate safeguarding practices can strain resources. For instance, addressing preventable harm or neglect requires additional interventions, investigations, and follow-up, diverting resources from other essential services.

- **Public trust and reputation**: Failing to safeguard patients and clients undermines public trust in healthcare institutions. Negative publicity and reputational damage can impact an organisation's credibility and ability to provide effective care.

To reduce these risks, healthcare professionals must prioritise prevention, early identification, and effective information-sharing. Remember that safeguarding is everyone's responsibility, and policies and procedures should ensure the safety and well-being of vulnerable individuals.

Reading and further research

Care Inspectorate Wales
https://www.careinspectorate.wales/

Disclosure and Barring Service
https://www.careinspectorate.wales/disclosure-and-barring-service-dbs-checks

National Independent Safeguarding Board Wales
https://safeguardingboard.wales/

Public Health Wales
https://phw.nhs.wales/

Values-based recruitment
https://heiw.nhs.wales/careers/nhs-wales-careers/experience-and-jobs/recruitment/

Whistleblowing – Raising Concerns about Healthcare in Wales
https://www.hiw.org.uk/whistleblowing-raising-concerns-about-healthcare-wales

6.6: How approaches in settings are used to meet individuals' needs and requirements

This chapter will be looking at how different approaches in health and social care settings in Wales are used to meet service users' needs and requirements. You will use the information included in this chapter, in addition to the research gathered from your sector engagement and/or work experience, to prepare your assignment.

What is an activity-based approach?

Some service users may spend considerable time in certain health and social care settings, or even live there as permanent residents. Whilst it is vital that high-quality care and support is carried out, it is also essential that service users are engaged in meaningful activities as often as possible.

There are many different approaches that can be used in health and social care settings that aim to have a positive effect on the health, well-being, and resilience of the service users. Depending on the activity, these can help with mobility, physical activity, cognitive ability, and isolation. An activity-based approach could include:

Physical activities – an activity using the body, usually to promote fitness and/or to improve mobility.

Intellectual and cognitive activities – an activity involving the use of thinking and/or memory skills.

Emotional activities – an activity that promotes or allows the expression of feelings and emotions.

Social activities – an activity that promotes personal relationships and communication with others.

Typical types of activities

- Gardening
- Drawing
- Reading
- Puzzles
- Cooking
- Knitting
- Exercise
- Music

One approach that may be used in health and social settings is an activity-based approach based on an individual's **life story** or an activity to allow **reminiscence therapy**. This method is especially successful with individuals living with memory loss or dementia. Usually, an individual living with dementia can remember and recall stories and events from many years ago, but is unable to recall recent events. Reminiscence therapy involves service users sharing their memories and their life stories. Such activities will boost the user's health, well-being, and resilience. This activity will give users a sense of belonging, identity and self-worth and can remind them of their contribution and value within the community or society.

Activity-based approaches in your sector engagement/ work experience placement

Whilst undertaking your sector engagement placement, you will need to identify activity-based approaches that are being implemented within the setting.

You could:

 ask the employer or senior staff for a menu of the different activities that are used for the service users at the health and social care setting

 be involved in the activities taking place to see how they are helping the service users' needs and requirements

 talk to the service users about the activities that they enjoy taking part in or the activities they would like to participate in

 implement an activity within the setting to support the needs and requirements of the service users (you will need to get permission from your employer to implement this suggestion)

What is Cognitive behavioural therapy (CBT)?

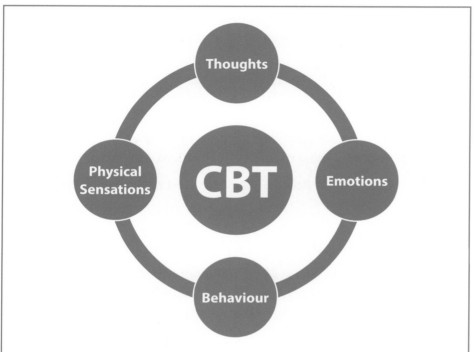

Cognitive behavioural therapy is a **talking therapy** used to treat individuals with anxiety, depression, and grief. It focuses on thoughts, emotions, behaviours, and physical sensations. A CBT approach can help to manage a problem by changing the way the individual thinks and behaves.

Cognitive behavioural therapy is a type of psychotherapy; it is used in health and social care settings to help service users to change the way they think, feel, and behave about or around certain things by talking. CBT focuses on the individual and focuses on them developing and using self-help strategies. The aim is that CBT will help individuals to improve their health, well-being and resilience, and evidence has shown it to be as effective as medication in treating certain mental health conditions. It's most commonly used to treat anxiety and depression, but can be a useful approach for other mental and physical health conditions.

Cognitive-based therapy is centred on the idea that thoughts, feelings and actions are interconnected, and that negative thoughts can trap an individual in a negative cycle. This approach aims to deal with a problem in a more positive way by dealing with one part of the problem at a time and by doing so, improve the way the individual feels about the problem. CBT aims to manage issues and to stop them having a negative impact on an individual's life.

Cognitive behaviour therapy in your sector engagement/work experience placement

Whilst undertaking your sector engagement placement, you will need to identify if **cognitive behaviour therapy (CBT)** is being used in the setting.

You could:

 ask the employer or senior staff if CBT is used at the setting for service users

 identify who is trained to carry out CBT in the setting, or who may attend the setting to deliver CBT sessions with the service users

 research online how CBT could be used within your setting

What is behaviour therapy?

Within health and social care settings, **behaviour therapy** can be used with service users to look at specific learned behaviours they may have, and how their environment influences those behaviours. Behaviour therapy may help in treating conditions such as eating disorders, self-harm, and substance misuse.

The aim of behaviour therapy is for the service user to learn new behaviours that will hopefully have a positive effect on their current behaviours. There are many different methods that can be used as part of a behaviour therapy strategy.

Behaviour therapy in your sector engagement/work experience placement

Whilst undertaking your sector engagement placement, you will need to identify if **behaviour therapy** is being used in the setting.

You could:

 ask the employer or senior staff if behaviour therapy is used with the service users

 identify who is trained to carry out behaviour therapy in the setting, or who may attend the setting to deliver behaviour therapy sessions with the service users

 research online how behaviour therapy could be used within your setting

What is positive behavioural support?

An understanding of the behaviour of an individual. It is based on an assessment of the social and physical environment in which the behaviour happens, and includes the views of the individual and everyone involved. It uses this understanding to develop support that improves the quality of life for the person and others who are involved with them.

www.bild.org.uk/pbs

Positive behavioural support may be used when individuals demonstrate **behaviours that challenge** or for individuals with learning disabilities. It is commonly used with service users who may challenge the care worker and/or the setting.

'Behaviours that challenge' is the description of a range of behaviours which some service users may display in order to ensure that the needs of those users are met, such as:

- **Hurting others** – hair-pulling, hitting, head-butting

- **Self-injury** – headbanging, eye-poking, hand-biting

- **Destructive behaviours** – throwing things, breaking furniture, tearing things

- **Eating inedible objects** – cigarette butts, pen lids, bedding

- **Other behaviours** – spitting, smearing, removing clothes in public, running off

Key components of positive behavioural support

Values	1	Prevention and reduction of behaviours that challenge occurs within the context of improving the quality of life, inclusion, participation and the defence and support of valued social roles.
	2	Constructional approaches to intervention by developing stakeholder skills and opportunities, and rejecting adverse and restrictive practices.
	3	Stakeholder participation informs, implements, and validates assessment and intervention practices.
Evidence-based theory and practice	4	An understanding of how behaviours that challenge serve important functions for individuals.
	5	The principles and procedures from behaviour analysis can be used to assess, and then support, behaviour change in individuals.
	6	The secondary use of other complementary, evidence-based approaches can also support behaviour change at multiple levels.
Process	7	A data-driven approach to decision-making at every stage.
	8	Functional assessment to inform function-based intervention.
	9	Multi-component interventions to change behaviour (proactively) and manage behaviour (reactively).
	10	Implementation of support, monitoring, and evaluation of interventions over the long term.

Positive behaviour support Stages 1–6:

1. Expectations
Set clear expectations

2. Modelling
Model positive behaviour

3. Consistency
Be consistent

4. Acknowledgement
Acknowledge positive efforts

5. Evaluation
Evaluate success

6.
… back to 1 re expectations

Positive behaviour support aims to improve the quality of life for individuals who have challenging behaviours. The approach focuses on understanding the underlying causes of the individuals' behaviour and looking for new strategies to improve the quality of their lives. This approach is very useful when dealing with an individual who is distressed and at risk of harming themselves and others.

It's a proactive and a person-centred approach that looks to their strengths, interests and challenges, with a focus on improving their well-being and dignity. Care workers need to work closely with the individual to understand why an individual is under stress and the factors and triggers that create that anxiety and stress. Based on their understanding, healthcare practitioners can then devise individualised strategies. The approach focuses on positive reinforcement and skill development, which is guided by evidence. It is worth remembering that positive behaviour support is one approach to improve the quality of life of an individual with challenging behaviours, and that different individuals may require a different type of support.

Positive behaviour support seen in your sector engagement placement

Whilst undertaking your sector engagement placement, you will need to identify if **positive behavioural support** is being used in the setting.

You could:

 ask the employer or senior staff if positive behavioural support is used with the service users

 identify who is trained to carry out positive behavioural support in the setting, or who may attend the setting to deliver behaviour therapy sessions with the service users

 research online how positive behavioural support could be used within your setting.

Checklist for the assignment

In preparation for your assignment, you must ensure that you have sourced the information about your setting or service to:

 explain how different approaches could be used in the setting or service to meet individuals' needs and requirements.

The Non-Examination Assessment – Task E

> **Explain how different approaches could be used in the setting/service to meet individuals' needs and requirements.**

Your answer must provide an explanation of how the different approaches to meet individuals' needs and requirements could be used in the setting or within the service. Your answer must, however, describe and reflect on the information you gathered based on your actual experiences during your sector engagement. You will also need to focus on how the theoretical approaches to meet patients' or clients' needs or requirements are used in practice in actual and real situations within the setting or service.

You will need to show that you know and understand how different approaches are used, or could be used, in care settings. These approaches could include the following:

- **Activity-based approaches**: This approach focuses on preventative care and on how to promote health by keeping patients and clients active and engaged in life. This engagement could include reminiscence therapy and 'life stories' that foster engagement and help individuals to stay healthy in mind and body.

- **Cognitive behaviour therapy (CBT):** This approach is a talking therapy that can help an individual to manage their problems by changing the way that an individual thinks and behaves.

- **Behaviour therapy**: This approach includes a wide range of different techniques that are used to reinforce desirable behaviours and eliminate undesirable behaviours. The aim of the approach is to change the behaviour of an individual. The individual often avoids a challenging situation, rather than confronting and dealing with it effectively. Examples of conditions that could respond positively to behaviour therapy can include eating disorders, self-harming behaviours, substance abuse and avoiding social situations due to anxiety or discomfort. These are all examples of maladaptive behaviours.

- **Learned behaviours**: Learned behaviours are behaviours that are modified by the learning process, observation and experience. They allow an individual to adapt to changes in the environment. This approach is developed through personal and social interaction.

- **Positive behavioural support**: This approach provides a method of supporting individuals, and involves understanding the reasons behind the behaviours, such as physical health, emotions and life history.

What the examiner is looking for

1   Candidates who explained the different types of approaches seen in their placement, and were able to explain how the approach theories were used in practice at the setting gained higher marks.

2   A detailed explanation of the specific types of approaches used when an individual shows behaviour that challenges in the context of your engagement placements.

6.7: How Welsh legislation impacts practice in health and social care settings

This chapter looks at the role of Welsh legislation and the impact it has on practice within health and social care settings in Wales. The background information included within this chapter, and your research during your engagement in the sector and the work experience, will assist you in preparing your assignment.

How does Welsh legislation, regulations and frameworks impact practice in health and social care settings in Wales?

All health and social care settings in Wales are required to implement legislation, regulations, and frameworks to help achieve the desired outcomes for a specific service and their service users.

Regulation and Inspection of Social Care (Wales) Act 2016

'The Act builds on the success of regulation in Wales and places the quality of services and improvement at the heart of regulation. It strengthens protection for those who need it, establishes a regulatory system that is in-line with the Social Services and Well-being (Wales) Act 2014, and creates a regulatory system that is centred around people who need care and support, and the social care workforce.'

This Act is about monitoring care and support services, to ensure that the quality of the services provided reflect the highest health and social care standards for the users of the services.

How does the Regulation and Inspection of Social Care (Wales) Act 2016 help to achieve the desired outcomes?

The provisions of the Regulation and Inspection of Social Care (Wales) Act 2016 focus on achieving the desired outcomes by:

- providing a framework for improvement in the care and the support provided for the users of the service in Wales

- creating a skilful and caring workforce to implement legislation and regulation within care and support settings in Wales

- establishing a well-being strategy, where the well-being of users is placed centre stage

- ensuring that all service providers are accountable and that all defects in the strategy are dealt with in an appropriate manner

- allowing all service users to be involved in offering feedback via a monitoring pathway.

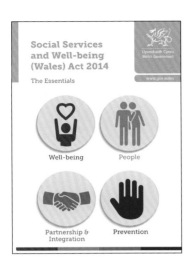

Social Services and Well-Being (Wales) Act 2014 (SSWA)

'The Social Services and Well-being (Wales) Act 2014 is a landmark piece of legislation for health and social care in Wales that will have implications for your work as a health and social care worker. It became law in 2014 and came into force in April 2016. It modernises and brings together different pieces of social care law.'

The Act provides the legal framework for improving the well-being of people who need care and support, and carers who need support, and for transforming social services in Wales.

The Act is built on the following core principles:

- Voice and control
- Prevention and early intervention
- Well-being
- Co-production
- Multi-agency

How does the Social Services and Well-Being (Wales) Act 2014 help to achieve the desired outcomes?

The aims of the Social Services and Well-being (Wales) Act 2014 include the following:

- to give service users a stronger voice and greater control of the support and services they receive to help them achieve feelings of well-being, care and support
- to ensure that timely advice and assistance is provided to service users to prevent things reaching a crisis point
- to provide early intervention and prevention by intervening early to help service users, to reduce or delay the need for longer term care and support
- to ensure that service users can ask for the help they need, when they need it, to prevent their situation becoming worse
- to support service users' right to well-being, by recognising that some will need help to achieve this goal.

Welsh Language (Wales) Measure 2011

'The Welsh Language (Wales) Measure 2011 (the Measure) modernised the existing legal framework for the use of the Welsh language in the delivery of public services.

It includes provision about the official status of the Welsh language and establishes the office of the Welsh Language Commissioner which replaced the Welsh Language Board.'

How does the Welsh Language (Wales) Measure 2011 help to achieve the desired outcomes?

The Act has **two principles** that will underpin the work of care workers in all health and social care settings in Wales:

1 The **Welsh language** should be treated **not be treated less favourably** than the English language.

2 Service users in Wales should be able to **live their lives** through the medium of the Welsh language, if they choose to do so.

Comisiynydd y
Gymraeg
Welsh Language
Commissioner

Cymraeg

Welsh Government 'More than words' and the 'Active Offer' 2016

'More than words' is the Welsh Government's strategic framework for promoting the Welsh language in the field of health and social care, and was published in 2016 . This framework identified the importance of receiving services through the medium of Welsh, as a core part of providing high-quality care that was based on human rights and providing a person-centred approach. This is a framework for people who live in a bilingual country. The framework also emphasised that for some people, using Welsh in health and social care is not only a matter of choice, but also a matter of need. Health and social care providers, therefore, have a responsibility to respond to these needs.

One of the most important aims of the framework is to ensure that people who need a Welsh-medium service receive an 'Active Offer', in terms of the use of the Welsh language. That is, that Welsh speakers can feel confident that their needs are being met. It is the responsibility of everyone who provides care services to people and children across Wales to place the person at the heart of health and social care services in Wales.

Mental Capacity Act 2005

Mental Capacity Act 2005

'If you can't make decisions for yourself because you don't have the mental capacity to make them, the Mental Capacity Act 2005 tells you:

- what you can do to plan ahead

- how you can ask someone else to make decisions for you

- who can make decisions for you if you haven't planned ahead.

The Mental Capacity Act will be important to you if you think that your ability to make certain decisions will be affected in the future because of your mental health problem, an illness, an injury, or outside reasons like the effect of the medication you are prescribed.'

How does the Mental Capacity Act 2005 help to achieve the desired outcomes?

The Act helps to achieve desired outcomes by helping to **assess** if an individual has mental capacity. As a service user, an individual will be assumed to have capacity, unless they have had an assessment showing otherwise. This helps individuals to achieve desired outcomes, by ensuring that service users who have lost their mental capacity will have all decisions made for them to be in their best interests.

Gathering information about how Welsh legislation, regulations and frameworks impacts daily procedures and practices in the setting

Whilst undertaking your sector engagement placement, you will need to identify how these Acts have been incorporated into the **daily procedures and practices** within your care setting.

You could:

 ask the employer, senior staff or fellow employees if they have knowledge and understanding of the Welsh legislation, regulations and frameworks relating to their setting

 make a detailed list of actual examples you have seen of Welsh legislation, regulations and frameworks being implemented by the setting during your work placement.

Activity

Use online methods to prepare background research for the following Acts:

- Regulation and Inspection of Social Care (Wales) Act 2016

- Social Services and Well-being (Wales) Act 2014

- Welsh Language (Wales) Measure 2011

- Mental Capacity Act 2005

Your research needs to identify the main features of these Acts, and what these Acts set out to achieve within care settings. In addition to your desktop research, you will also need to include your work experience placement and use examples of the legislation from your own experience, to show that the legislation and regulations are being followed.

How are health and social care providers in Wales inspected and regulated?

Health and social care settings in Wales are inspected and regulated to ensure that professional standards and guidance are being followed at all times, ensuring that the setting and care workers are providing a high quality of care.

Care Inspectorate Wales (CIW)

Care Inspectorate Wales registers, inspects and acts to improve the quality and safety of services in all care settings in Wales, for the well-being of the people of Wales.

Care Inspectorate Wales carries out inspections of care settings in Wales to provide assurance on the quality and safety within those settings.

It regulates the following services:

Adult services	Care homes for adults, domiciliary support services, adult placement services and residential family centre services.
Children's services	Care homes for children, fostering services, adoption services, advocacy services and secure accommodation services.
Childcare and play services	Child minders, crèches, full day care, sessional day care, out of school care and open-access play provision.
Other local authorities' settings	Local authority fostering and adoption services, boarding schools, residential special schools (boarding arrangements under 295 days), further education colleges with residential accommodation for students under 18.

Care Inspectorate Wales aims to:

- help the quality and safety of care settings by deciding **who** can provide health and care services in Wales

- carry out regular **inspections**

- **drive improvement** of regulated services and local authority social services

- undertake **national reviews** of social care services and **take action** to ensure services meet legislative and regulatory requirements.

Healthcare Inspectorate Wales (HIW)

agic | Arolygiaeth Gofal Iechyd Cymru
hiw | Healthcare Inspectorate Wales

Healthcare Inspectorate Wales (HIW) is the independent inspectorate and regulator of healthcare in Wales. It inspects NHS services and regulates independent healthcare providers against a range of standards, policies, guidance, and regulations to highlight areas requiring improvement.

How are health and social care providers in Wales inspected and regulated?

Healthcare Inspectorate Wales regulates many health services in Wales, including the following:

Hospitals, hospices, GP services, dental, mental health and learning disability, ionising radiation (e.g. radiotherapy), laser – surgical (e.g. laser eye surgery), laser – non-surgical (e.g. hair or tattoo removal), circumcision, IVF and termination of pregnancy.

Social Care Wales (SCW)

 Gofal Cymdeithasol **Cymru**
Social Care **Wales**

Social Care Wales keeps a register of care workers in Wales, who have shown that they are suitable to work in social care. Everyone on the Register must show that they are:

- appropriately qualified
- physically and mentally fit to practise
- have the character and competence to practise
- able to follow the Code of Professional Practice for Social Care (the Code) and practice guidance for their role
- intend to practise social care in Wales.

Gathering information about regulation and inspection during your work experience or service placement

Whilst undertaking your sector engagement placement, you will need to identify how the care setting is **regulated** and **inspected** and with who the care workers need to be registered.

You could:

 ask team members and read internal policy and procedure documents on how the care setting is regulated and inspected.

 research online for their latest inspection report. You should be able to access service inspection reports for your placement setting /service, as these are public documents

 ask the care workers who they are registered with

 research online who regulates each specific job role within the setting.

Health and care settings in Wales follow inspection frameworks set out by Care Inspectorate Wales and Healthcare Inspectorate Wales, to ensure that well-being goals and outcomes are being achieved.

**Care Inspectorate Wales
Inspection Framework**

https://www.careinspectorate.wales/providing-
a-care-service/our-inspections

**Healthcare Inspectorate Wales
Inspection Framework**

www.hiw.org.uk

The Inspection Framework affecting practice in the setting during your sector engagement/ work experience placement

Whilst undertaking your sector engagement placement, you will need to access your setting's latest **inspection report** and see the **Framework** that they follow.

You could:

 interview the employer to find out how the Inspection Framework impacts on their practice in the setting

 research online for their latest inspection report

Checklist for your assignment

When you are preparing your assignment, you must make sure that you have sourced your information within your setting or service. You will need the following details for your assignment:

 show how Welsh legislation, regulations and frameworks have influenced practice in the setting or service to improve outcome focused person-centred care

 inform policy and practice to achieve desired outcomes for health and social care workers and individuals accessing the care

 use examples from your sector engagement experiences to illustrate your answer.

Non-Examination Assessment – Task A(iii)

> **Consider how Welsh legislation, regulations and frameworks have influenced practices in the setting/service to:**
>
> **1. Improve outcome-focused person-centred care**
>
> **Use examples from your sector engagement to illustrate your answer.**
>
> **2. Inform policy and practice to achieve the desired outcomes for health and social care workers and individuals accessing the care.**

1. Improve outcome-focused person-centred care

Your answer should focus on illustrating how Welsh legislation, regulations and frameworks influence policies and procedures within the setting or service that you have directly experienced as part of sector engagement. You will need to focus on including actual examples of how Welsh legislation, regulations and frameworks are being applied within your setting or service during your sector placement. You will need to consider how the following legislation, regulations and frameworks have focused on strengthening a person-centred approach. Your answer could refer to the following:

- Regulation and Inspection of Social Care (Wales) Act 2016
- Social Services and Well-Being (Wales) Act 2014 (SSWA)
- Welsh Language (Wales) Measure 2011
- Mental Capacity Act 2005
- Inspection frameworks and what is required by settings to achieve positive achievements and outcomes for the well-being of the patients or clients and the health and social care providers at the setting.
- The role of Care Inspectorate Wales (CIW) and Healthcare Inspectorate Wales (HIW) in ensuring that health and social care are regulated and inspected to enable providers to achieve professional standards and guidance for practitioners.
- The 'More than just words…' and the 'Active Offer' initiative by the Welsh Government in 2016.

You will need to describe and evaluate how Welsh legislation, regulations and frameworks have influenced the outcome of achieving a person-centred approach by both providers and practitioners. The desired outcome of a person-centred approach in health and social care involves the health and social care sector working in partnership with the individuals using the services. Has the setting or the service enabled the patients or clients to feel empowered and manage their own health, make informed decisions and feeling confident in the care they receive? Has the Welsh legislation, regulations and frameworks led to each person being treated as a unique individual, and does it reflect their unique needs and expectations?

2. Inform policy and practice to achieve the desired outcomes for health and social care workers and individuals accessing the care.

Your answer will need to focus on how the health and social care team are informed about the legislation, regulations and frameworks, which affect the policies and procedures applied within the setting or service. What are mechanisms used by the health and social care providers for informing the staff of existing legislation, regulations and frameworks? Do these mechanisms include induction sessions and regular on-going in-service training sessions? What are the monitoring and evaluation arrangements within the setting or service? Are the staff aware of CIW and HIW inspection policies and procedures in establishing and monitoring desired outcomes for health and social care workers?

Are patients and clients informed of the policies and procedures in place, to ensure that they receive a care service that is focusing on their individual needs and aspirations? What is the evidence from your placement that individuals are aware of their rights as set out in Welsh legislation, regulations and frameworks? For this assessment task, you need to evaluate Welsh legislation, regulatory practices and frameworks to demonstrate your understanding of their role in practice at the setting or service. You will need to use actual examples of how legislation, regulations and frameworks influence the policies, procedures and practice of the setting or service.

What the examiner is looking for

1   You should refer to the legislation, regulatory practices and frameworks outlined in the specification to achieve higher mark band outcomes.

2   You will lose potential marks for not relating legislation, regulations, frameworks, and practice to your specific sector or setting experience. You will need to include actual examples from your work experience to illustrate how these are applied.

3   You will need to refer in detail to the legislation which is specific to Wales, e.g., Social Services and Well-being (Wales) Act 2014 (SSWA), Welsh Language (Wales) Measure 2011 and the Welsh Government strategic framework 'More than just words' and the 'Active Offer' published in 2016. More emphasis should be placed on Welsh legislation, regulations and frameworks for this specific assessment, as opposed to more general legislation such as the Human Rights Act, which relates to a wider UK audience.

Reading and further research

Mental Capacity Act 2005
https://www.legislation.gov.uk/ukpga/2005/9/contents

Regulation and Inspection of Social Care (Wales) Act 2016
https://socialcare.wales/resources-guidance/information-and-learning-hub/regulation-and-inspection/overview

Care Inspectorate Wales
https://www.careinspectorate.wales/sites/default/files/2019-06/190620-inspection-framework-en_0.pdf

Healthcare Inspectorate Wales
www.hiw.org.uk

Welsh Language (Wales) Measure 2011
https://www.legislation.gov.uk/mwa/2011/1/contents

'More than just words' – Welsh Government's strategic framework for promoting the Welsh language in health and social care in 2016
https://www.careinspectorate.wales/more-just-words

'Active Offer'
https://www.gov.wales/sites/default/files/publications/2019-04/delivering-the-active-offer-information-pack-health_0.pdf

Social Services and Well-being (Wales) Act 2014
https://www.legislation.gov.uk/cy/anaw/2014/4/contents

Social Care Wales
https://socialcare.wales/registration

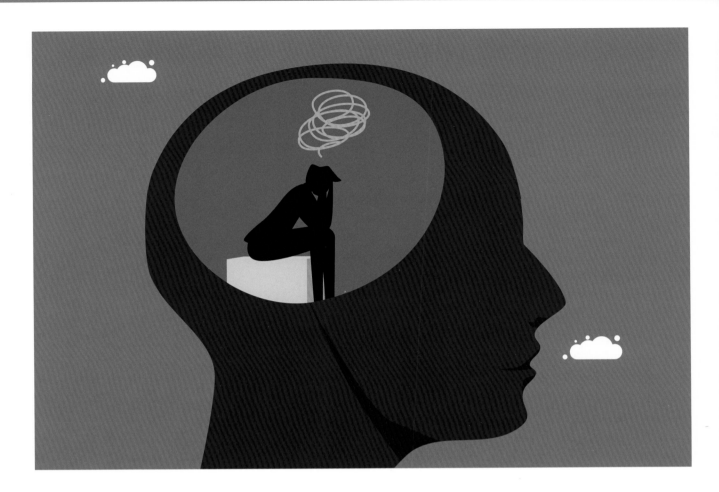

6.8: The role of reflection in care settings

Key terms

Reflection and reflective practice
An individual thinking about what they are doing or have done.

Professional development
An opportunity for an individual to learn a new or develop an existing skill that will enhance carrying out their job role.

This chapter looks at the role of regular reflection and reflective practice in care settings. You will use the information in this chapter and the research gathered from your sector engagement and/or work experience to prepare your assignment.

What is reflection and reflective practice?

Reflection and reflective practice refer to an individual thinking about what they do or have done. This process involves reviewing and analysing. Reflective practices should be encouraged in all settings to allow care workers to identify their strengths and weaknesses.

Most health and social care settings will have identified reflection processes within their policies and procedures to ensure that care workers can build on and improve their practice. Reflection also considers the care worker's needs, and reflective practice should contribute to their professional development. Time should be set aside for reflective practice meetings between an individual worker and their manager. Reflective practice meetings may take place weekly, monthly or annually, and will look at improving the care worker's practice. Each setting will have a responsibility to ensure that each care worker continues to develop their own skills and abilities.

Reflective diary

During your work experience placement, you will be required to complete and submit a **Reflective diary**. This will give you an opportunity to reflect on your own practice. During your work experience placement, you will need to take time to reflect at the end of each day. Your diary will need to identify the **reflection** and **reflective practices** within the setting. Your diary could, for example, involve you asking yourself the following type of questions:

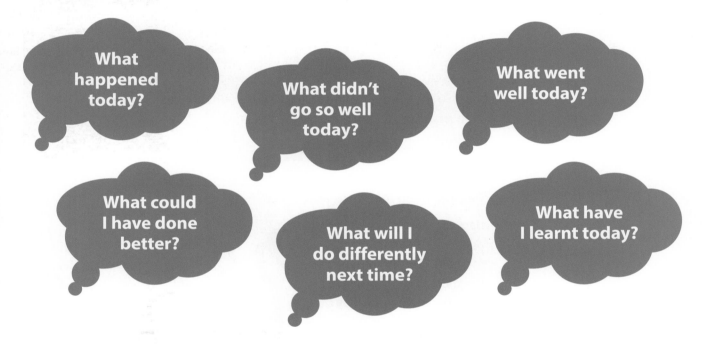

You will also need to:

 ask the employer or a member of the senior staff about their reflection and reflective practice processes within the location

 ask for a copy of the reflection and reflective practice policies for the location

 discuss with the care workers about how their reflection and reflective practice processes work and why the process is useful for their own professional development.

How can reflection and reflective practice be implemented within a care setting?

Reflection and reflective practice can be implemented by using a variety of different methods. Most settings will use more than one method for their reflection and reflective processes. These methods include:

Individuals preparing a reflective diary

A reflective diary can be used by a care worker to record their experiences of a significant event that had taken place or to simply record the events of that day.

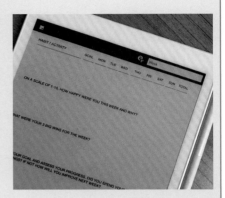

The reflective diary will give the care worker the opportunity to write the positives and negatives of the event or the events of the day.

The care worker will also be able to use the diary to record what they have learnt from the event, and also what they would need to do to improve their practice if that were to happen again.

reMarkable – Daily Reflection Journal Template – Einkpads

Regular team meetings and discussions

Regular team meetings and discussions can be used for reflection and reflective practice, as it will provide the care workers with an opportunity to collectively discuss their current practice.

Being given time to come together as a team can be vital in sharing positives and concerns that they may have, whilst also giving care workers an opportunity to share ways for achieving improvement.

Agendas for Interdisciplinary Team Meetings
Home Centred Care Institute (hccinstitute.org)

Observations by senior colleagues

In many care settings, care workers will be observed by senior colleagues.

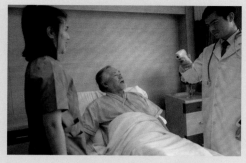

This method for reflection and reflective practice is an excellent way to observe care staff practice and to provide valuable feedback for the staff. This exercise can be a great way of sharing good practice, as it provides a mechanism for all team members to work in partnership, which can provide a basis for reflection and reflective practice; this in turn leads to achieving the highest standards of care.

Appraisals, supervisions, and performance management reviews for social care:

Appraisal is a more formal process that involves the review of a social care worker's performance and improvement over a period of time (usually annually).

All care workers will have appraisals, supervisions, and performance management reviews in relation to their job role. These are methods to ensure that care workers are carrying out their duties by monitoring their performance. The purpose of performance management is continuous improvement to both the care worker and the setting.

These methods should help care workers to identify targets for improvements and look at ways to address them. These targets will then be monitored to see how well the targets have been met, and to see if they have been met in an effective way.

The Care Council for Wales have produced a useful guide: *Supervising and Appraising Well: A Guide to Effective Supervision and Appraisal for those working in Social Care.*

Awareness, self-reflection, and the impact on self

Another method for reflection and reflective practice is through awareness, self-reflection, and the impact on yourself.

Self-reflection will allow care workers to learn about themselves. It will enable them to become aware of their own abilities and strengths, whilst giving them an opportunity to become aware of the areas of improvements and the abilities they need to improve.

This method should help staff to focus on their care practice, and also improve their skills and abilities within the care setting, allowing them to become more effective in their job role.

heiw.nhs.wales/files/benefits-of-becoming-a-reflective-practitioner/

Gathering information about reflection and reflective practice during your work experience or service placement

Whilst undertaking your sector engagement placement, you will need to identify the **reflection** and **reflective practice** methods used within the setting.

You could:

 Ask the employer, or senior staff members, about the reflection and reflective practices used within the setting so that you can gather detailed information about the practices used at the location.

 Interview care workers within the setting and find out about their own reflective and reflection practices at the location.

 Ask the employer or senior staff members for a template or a copy of their reflection and reflective practices.

Models and theories of reflective practice

There are different models and theories when it comes to reflective practice, and each one has a different method for reflecting on practice. Care workers may use different models and theories whilst conducting their roles, to reflect on their practice.

Kolb-reflective cycle model

David Kolb's reflective cycle is a widely used and accepted model of reflective practice within the care sector. Kolb stated that we learn from our experiences; he produced a cycle that consisted of four stages: Experience, Reflection, Conceptualise and Planning.

Concrete experience	A person having a new experience which may influence their learning.
Reflective observation	Reflective observation includes watching others or developing observations about your own experiences. What are your thoughts about this experience and its relationship with your learning?
Abstract conceptualisation	Abstract conceptualisation is about developing theories to explain observations. How would you conceptualise your thoughts?
Active experimentation	Active experimentation is about using theories to solve problems and making decisions. What impact does this newly achieved learning outcome have on your future learning?

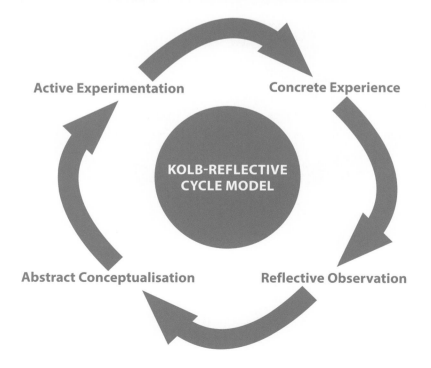

Active Experimentation

Concrete Experience

KOLB-REFLECTIVE CYCLE MODEL

Abstract Conceptualisation

Reflective Observation

Honey and Mumford Model

Peter Honey and Alan Mumford developed a reflection model in which the learner is the reflector. They developed a questionnaire that divides people into four distinct types of learners under the headings 'Activists', 'Reflectors', 'Theorists' and 'Pragmatists'. Most individuals show a dominant preference for one or two styles of learning.

Activists	These are 'go-getters'. They are flexible, learn by doing, and they enjoy new experiences and opportunities to learn.
Reflectors	They watch, reflect, and take time to consider. They learn by observing and then thinking about what happened.
Theorists	Know the facts thoroughly before applying knowledge; they learn best when they understand the theory behind their actions.
Pragmatists	Practical and realistic, they like to try things out and see if they work. They like to experiment with ideas, theories and materials to see if they work in real-life situations.

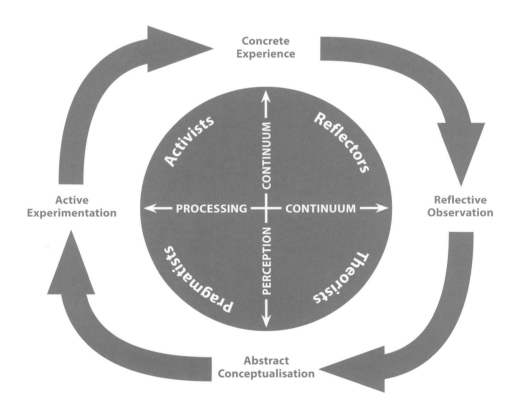

Schön-reflection model

Donald Schön developed a reflection model that was based on the notion that reflecting needs to take place during the experience itself. Schön stated that it was important that individuals think about what they are doing, while they are doing it. Schön looked at the importance of reflection during the experience ('reflection-in-action') and reflecting on that action ('reflection-on-action').

Reflection-in-action	Reflecting during the experience ■ thinking ahead ■ analysing ■ experiencing ■ critically responding
Reflection-on-action	Reflecting after the experience ■ thinking through subsequent situations ■ discussion ■ reflective journal

Gathering information about the use of reflection models during your period of work experience placement in a setting or service

Whilst undertaking your sector engagement placement, you will need to identify if any of the **reflection models** are used in practice.

You could:

 ask the employer or senior staff members if they use reflection models for their reflection and reflective practices within the location

 find out more about the models by using online research, and see if they could be appropriate for their reflection and reflective practices within the location

 choose one of the models to study in detail to see if that model could provide an appropriate model to reflect on your experiences at the setting.

Checklist for the assignment

You must ensure that **you have sourced the information from the location itself** in order to complete the assignment. Sources can be included in the text, and also within a bibliography.

You can use the following guidelines to assist you with your assignment:

 Explain how reflective practice supports the professional development of health and social care workers within the setting or the service.

 With reference to relevant theorists, explain how health and social care teams within the setting or service can reflect on their practice when assessing and improving the care and support they provide to individuals and their families.

Non-Examination Assessment Section F Task F(i)

The N.E.A. Section F Task F(i)

Explain how reflective practice supports the professional development of health and social care workers within the setting or service.

The N.E.A. Section F Task F(ii)

With reference to relevant theorists, explain how health and social care teams within the setting or service can reflect on their practice when assessing and improving the care and support they provide to individuals and their families.

Non-Examination Assessment Section F Task F(i)

Explain how reflective practice supports the professional development of health and social care workers within the setting or service.

Your response to this question must provide an explanation of how reflective practice supports the professional development of health and social care workers within the setting or service. You will need to record your actual experiences during your sector engagement. Explain in detail how reflection on processes, policies and procedures can improve practice and professional development. Your response could include the following:

- How does reflective practice support the professional development of individual health and social care workers within the location or service?

- How do health and social care workers at the location or service use reflective practices to continually improve their practice?

- What is the evidence that reflective practices at the setting contribute to the ongoing learning and professional development of team members?

- Based on what has been learnt during reflective practices, what are the arrangements for reviewing documents, policies, procedures and practice in the setting?

- Are there opportunities provided by the setting to allow individual members to inform senior management and fellow staff members of the lessons learnt during reflection and reflective practices?

Non-Examination Assessment Section F Task F(ii)

With reference to relevant theorists, explain how health and social care teams within the setting or service can reflect on their practice when assessing and improving the care and support they provide to individuals and their families.

Your answer must provide an **explanation** of how health and social care teams within the setting or service have an opportunity to reflect by using relevant reflective models. What are the reflective models used at the setting to reflect on their practice? How are these reflective models being used to assess and improve the care and support they provide to individuals and their families? You will need to by provide an overview of the reflective models and how they are used by the setting, and explain how they are used in practice, based on your experience at the setting.

A large number of models and theories have been developed for reflective practice. They include, for example, **Honey and Mumford**, **Kolb**, **Schön**, **Gibbs**, **Driscoll**, **Johns** and **Jasper**.

You will also need to explain the different ways in which reflective practice takes place in health and care settings. These include:

- individual team members writing a reflective diary

- providing regular team meetings with an open invitation to discuss and share experiences, and reflect on how a recent experience can lead to providing a better level of care for their patients or clients

- arranging regular team meetings to facilitate feedback and establish an open relationship with senior colleagues and management. This reflective practice could provide an opportunity for all staff within the setting or service to work in partnership to improve health and care practice for the benefit of all service users

- holding staff appraisals, supervision sessions and performance management reviews, which could include an opportunity for reflection and strengthening reflection practices

- providing opportunities for an individual to undertake self-reflection and prepare a personal action plan

- arranging dedicated sessions on reflective practice to inform and evaluate different models and theories.

What the examiner is looking for

For assessment task F(i):

1   Your answer must provide an **explanation** of how health and social care teams within the setting or service can reflect on their practice when assessing and improving the care and support they provide to individuals and their families.

2   You will need to gather detailed **evidence** of reflective practice seen in your work placement.

3   You will need to gather evidence of how reflection and reflective practice plays a part in **employee professional development**, and how this impacts **health and social care practice** in the location or service.

4   You must remember to **explain**, rather than **describe**, how reflection and reflective practices are applied in professional development practice at the setting.

5   You will need to **plan** and **prepare in advance** of gathering the evidence for this assessment task. Plan carefully in terms what information you will require to enable you to respond fully to the requirements of the assessment task. This will also require you to have knowledge of the models and theories so that you can ask the participants the right questions.

For assessment task F(ii):

1   Using your **reflective diary** to apply knowledge and understanding of theories such as Kolb, Honey and Mumford and Schön, or other reflective models and theories, will achieve higher marks.

2   Referring to a relevant theorist, you need to **explain** how reflection practices can be a valuable tool during the process of assessing and improving health and social care in the setting. Higher marks can also be achieved by referring to your reflective diary, written during your engagement placement. Your reflective diary can enhance your **ability to assess the value** of reflection models and theories in strengthening personal reflection and in improving practice.

3   Additional reference to the value of **personalised action planning**, **team meetings** and **performance management** in the setting also succeeded in gaining higher marks.

4   Reference to the value of reflective practice as a **quality assurance mechanism**, which led to an improvement in outcome-focused care also gained additional marks.

5   Including a detailed **bibliography**, to evidence your secondary source research is also good practice. Also, sources can be cited in-text within your written NEA response.

Sample response of a candidate and the examiner's comments examiner

Candidate response: (in their own words)

With health and social care, Schön's theory can be linked to health and social care. This theory is about reflection. This can be important for health and social care staff when trying to reflect on their practices. All professionals should do some sort of reflective practice. This can be by producing an individual reflective diary, or even going to programmes about reflection. Another theory that can be used when explaining why it's important that staff should reflect is the Honey and Mumford theory. This theory is about how it has the ability to allow individuals to have a better understanding of themselves and their abilities. This can be a good theory as they will be able to learn different things about themselves and be able to focus on the different things they could improve. Fundamental needs and rights can be important for them. It means that they get the best sort of protection, and their needs have to be met before they can try to achieve higher potentials.

With Schön's theory it will allow professionals to feel better in themselves and will allow them to improve the care and support of individuals and their families. It will also allow them to gain higher potential of doing well.

Multi-disciplinary teams can assess and improve care and support as it involves healthcare professions that come together as a team and plan and coordinate peoples individualised care. Any type of work in the health and social care sector can be part of the multi-disciplinary team. This can be related to families as it will allow the families to know that the individuals will be getting the best care. It can bring families together. With the professionals reflecting on their practice this can be by collaborating. (Macmillan, S.S., Pedro Morago, Linda Bruce and Malcolm,N.D.)

Bibliography references for Unit 6: (only part shown):

www.hse.gov.uk. (n.d.). *Employer's responsibilities: Workers' health and safety*.

Cqc.org.uk. (2014). *Regulation 7: Requirements relating to registered managers | Care Quality Commission*. [online] Available at: **https://www.cqc.org. uk/guidance-providers/regulations-enforcement/regulation-7-requirements-relating-registered-managers**

Examiner's comments:

The response shows in-text referencing and a bibliography. The candidate presented some knowledge and understanding in reference to the work of a few named theorists. However, the knowledge and understanding were not specifically applied to the sector engagement placement, and the overall structuring of the response could have been improved.

Glossary

Abuse: A child or adult being abused by someone else in a way that results in cruelty, violence or aggression.

Active communication: A method of communication that involves understanding and interpreting what is transmitted through non-verbal speech or communication.

Active Offer: The 'Active Offer' is a concept in Wales that means providing a service in Welsh without someone having to ask for it. It means that the Welsh language should be as visible and heard as the English language. 'The 'Active Offer' aims to create a change in culture that takes the responsibility off the patient to ask for a service through the medium of Welsh.

Active participation: The Code of Professional Practice for Social Care has defined active participation as a way of working that views individuals as 'active partners in their own care, rather than passive individuals. Active participation recognises the right of each individual to engage in activities of daily living, as independently as possible'.

Acute infections: These infections usually appear unannounced and normally last for a short period of time, e.g. flu.

Adult at risk: The term "adult at risk" has replaced "vulnerable adult". According to the Care Act 2014, an adult at risk is someone aged 18 or over. These adults at risk often need community care services due to a mental disability or other disability, their age, illness, or not being able to take care of themselves. They are also often unable to protect themselves from harm, while others can take advantage of them.

Advocacy: A service that provides a voice for all individuals to have their say about the care and support they receive.

Aging process: Aging is the process of getting older. At the biological level, aging results from the impact of a wide variety of molecular damage and damage to the cells over time. This leads to a gradual decrease in physical and mental ability, with an increased risk of disease.

Allegation: When a person or other person tells you they are being abused, or have been abused.

Allergy: Allergies, also known as allergic diseases, are various conditions caused by the immune system's hypersensitivity to typically harmless substances in the environment. These diseases include hay fever, food allergy, atopic dermatitis, allergic asthma, and anaphylaxis.

Appraisal: An act of assessing someone or something. It can be a formal assessment, such as an interview to measure an employee's performance over a period of time.

Assessment: A method of evaluating what care and support a person needs. This care and support will be different for each individual.

Asthma: A lung condition that leads to breathing problems.

Auto-immune disease: A physiological condition that occurs when the mechanism that enables the immune system to recognise the difference between the body's cells and external cells breaks down. This causes the body to attack its own cells, in error.

Bacterial infections: A bacterial infection is any illness or condition caused by bacterial growth or toxins. They are caused by small single-celled organisms called bacteria that spread in the body. The spread of harmful bacteria causes a bacterial infection. Bacterial infections can affect any part of the body, including the skin, gut, lungs, heart, brain and blood.

Behaviour therapy: Behaviour therapy offers numerous benefits for mental health and well-being. It helps individuals to manage their emotions, by being taught coping strategies and relaxation techniques. It can also improve relationships by addressing negative behaviours, leading to better interaction with others. The therapy focuses on encouraging positive behaviours and improving relationships with family, friends and others. The therapy can be useful for treating several conditions, such as eating disorders, self-harm and substance abuse.

Building a relationship: Establishing a connection with a person. This usually happens at the beginning of a relationship. It is based on mutual trust and involves finding common ground. It shows that you are communicating with that person, and that you are willing to listen to them, to establish a relationship with them.

Cardiovascular system: The cardiovascular system, also known as the circulatory system, is responsible for pumping blood throughout the body. The system includes the heart, blood vessels, and blood. The heart sends oxygen-rich blood through the arteries of the body, while the veins transport oxygen-deficient blood back to the heart.

Care and support plan: A plan prepared by a social worker for an individual (and their family or carer) who needs support. The plan sets out what is important to the individual, and what helps the individual to be as independent as possible, to secure her/his welfare, fulfil his/her wishes and, personal hopes and support their development.

Care Inspectorate Wales: Responsibility for reviewing and inspecting the NHS and independent healthcare organisations in Wales.

Care worker stress: This is a condition characterised by physical, mental and emotional exhaustion. It usually originates from a care worker neglecting their own physical and emotional health because the caregiver is so focused on caring for a person who is sick, or injured or disabled. Care workers under stress may experience fatigue, anxiety and depression. All care workers are at risk of stress and fatigue, regardless of their skill level, commitment and determination. Care workers often experience more stress than the patient they are caring for.

Carer: A person who provides support to an adult or a disabled child. The legal definition of a carer states that a person is not a carer if that person provides care under contract, or as voluntary work.

Child at risk: A 'child at risk' is a child who is being abused or at risk of abuse. The child is often a neglected child, or a child who is suffering other kinds of harm. A child at risk is a child with specific needs for care and support.

Chronic infections: These infections can last over months or years, e.g. osteomyelitis.

Chronic Obstructive Pulmonary Disease (COPD): A group of diseases characterised by long-term respiratory symptoms and airflow constraints.

Code of Practice: A code of practice is a set of written rules that explains how people working in a particular profession should behave.

Code of Practice for NHS Wales Employers: The Code of Practice for NHS Wales Employers is an important assurance mechanism, supporting the employment of Healthcare Support Workers in Wales. The Code of Practice for Employers is supported by a Code of Conduct for Healthcare, Support Workers that describes the Standards that individuals must comply with.

Code of Professional Practice for Social Care: The purpose of the Code is to ensure that health and social care workers in Wales provide quality care and support to their patients and clients. The Code requires all employees to register, to ensure that they are suitable and are able to practice in the sector. The Code contains a set of rules, or standards, that care professionals must practice in order to keep the patient or client safe and healthy.

Cognitive behaviour therapy: Cognitive behavioural therapy is a type of talk therapy or psychotherapy that is used to treat a variety of conditions with the objective of changing the way a person thinks or associates thoughts and feelings towards a particular subject. CBT is based on behavioural and cognitive psychotherapies that challenge negative thoughts around thinking patterns contributing to the way things are seen, felt or experienced. By participating in guided sessions, individuals can learn to analyse and question their usual thought patterns and behaviours, replacing them with more beneficial and constructive alternatives. This approach helps them address their immediate concerns, and equips them with a valuable skill set to manage life's challenges in a balanced and health-conscious way.

Collaboration: Two or more individuals or groups working together to achieve specific goals through the exchange of ideas and experiences.

Communicable condition: A condition that can be passed from one individual to another.

Communicate: Communication skills are abilities and techniques used to exchange information, ideas, and feelings effectively. Communication skills involve listening, speaking, observing, and showing empathy.

Communicative approaches: Different methods of interacting with the patient or client through speech, non-verbal communication, visual or other communication methods.

Competence: The ability to use and apply the knowledge, skills and behaviours that have been learnt to provide excellent care in health and social care settings.

Conceptualise: Form an idea or principle in your mind.

Confidentiality: A requirement not to disclose information about a patient's medical or private details, or clientele to others without their consent.

Co-production: Co-production across the NHS refers to engaging patients, their families, and communities, as they design and deliver healthcare services. It is used in situations where health care providers recognise that they need to work in partnership with patients and those who use the service to plan and deliver quality care.

Dementia: A variety of conditions that affect how a person thinks, remembers, solves problems, uses language and communicates. These conditions occur when the brain cells cease to function as they should, and the brain is damaged by disease.

Depression: A medical condition that causes low mood that affects the mind and spirit. It can be for a short period of time or a longer term, that is more serious. That condition affects the person's daily life.

Diabetes: A health condition that occurs when blood glucose (sugar) is too high. Diabetes is a chronic disease that occurs either when the pancreas does not produce enough insulin, or when the body cannot effectively use the insulin it produces.

Diagnosis and monitoring a condition: This includes looking at the person's medical history, body examination, taking a scan (CT, MRI, Ultrasound, PET

and SPECT) and X-ray scan, blood and urine tests, or minor surgery (taking a biopsy for example). The diagnosis will then need to be monitored by multi-disciplinary and/or multi-agency teams.

Digestive system: The digestive system involved in ingesting, digesting and absorbing food and disposing of waste. It involves the digestive tract, which is the series of organs through which food and fluids pass and glands and organs that release different juices and enzymes. The digestive tract extends from the mouth to the anus and includes the mouth, teeth, tongue, pharynx, stomach and intestines. Glands and other organs that make up the digestive system include the pancreas, liver and the gallbladder.

Dignified care: Care that respects each person's choices/decisions and considers how they would like to be treated. Care that treats people respectfully without undermining their self-esteem or self-worth. Allowing a person to choose what they want to wear or how they wish to be greeted for example.

Dignity: Care with dignity supports the self-respect of the person, recognising their capacities and ambitions, and does nothing to undermine it. It includes respect for what they can do, who they are, and the life they've lived. It's seen as a central part of quality in health and care work and settings.

Disclosure and Barring Service (DBS): The Disclosure and Barring Service (DBS) helps employers make safer recruitment decisions, and prevent unsuitable people from working with children or vulnerable adults. A DBS Check will check if there is a criminal record or other evidence available on individuals working with children and adults.

Disclosure of abuse: When someone tells you that abuse has happened, or is happening.

Discrimination: Unethical treatment of an individual or group.

Discrimination based on association: An individual's association with another individual belonging to a relevant protected group, such as: age, disability, gender re-determination, race, religion or belief, gender and sexual orientation.

Discrimination based on perception: Discrimination against someone because of a mistaken perception of a protected characteristic.

Discriminatory practice: The Equality Act 2010 legally protects people from discrimination in the workplace and within society.

Diversity: Diversity in health and social care refers to the presence of individuals from various backgrounds, cultures, ethnicities, genders, sexual orientations, religions, ages, and abilities within the sector. It means recognising and respecting differences in ethnicity, language, culture, faith, sexuality, gender identity, and socioeconomic background. Diversity is important in health and social care because it means that services can be tailored to meet the needs of a wide range of people.

Duty of care: It is the responsibility of the health and social care worker to look after each individual. There is a duty to abide by legal and moral requirements for the benefit of the individual in their care.

Duty of honesty: A responsibility to always be honest and truthful in relation to the patient or client.

Effective communication: This is the art of exchanging information in a way that fosters understanding, collaboration and interaction. It's more than words, it's about clarity and creating an environment conducive to dialogue.

Emotional distress: A state of mental pain that can include a variety of symptoms. Emotional distress can result from a mental health problem or a specific issue, such as a challenging relationship issue or financial stress. Emotional distress is a broad term that can include a variety of mental health disorders.

Empathy: Seeing things from someone else's point of view or perspective to understand their situation and feelings.

Employer: The establishment or individual(s) employing health and social care staff. Employers have a 'duty of care' towards their employees under health and safety law. This means that employers have a responsibility to protect their employees' health, safety and well-being at work.

Empowerment: Supporting individuals to deal with problems and to take responsibility for their own lives and make their own decisions.

Endrocrine system: The endocrine system is a network of glands that produce and secrete hormones into the circulatory system, regulating the functioning of the system. Endocrine glands work without ducts for carrying secretions towards target organs. Instead, hormones can act as chemical messengers for a large number of cells and tissues simultaneously.

Enforcement: The act of enforcing obedience and compliance and certain legislation, regulations or requirements applicable to the location or service.

Engagement: Patient engagement is defined as the steps people take to support their own health and how best to benefit from health care. Engagement involves placing a responsibility on patients and others to eat healthily and stay fit in partnership with those who offer advice and care. Engagement is increasingly recognised as an integral part of healthcare and social care, and a critical element in offering a safe and a person-centred approach.

Epilepsy: Epilepsy results from abnormal activity in the brain. It can affect any part of the brain.

Equity of access: Making sure everyone has equal opportunities that fit their requirements. Everyone is different, so it is essential that each individual receives the service that fits their requirements. This will require flexibility to create a programme which is specially designed for that person. The programme will need to ensure that the person who requires equality of access has access to that service.

Ethical values: Ethical values considers how health professionals, researchers and policy makers prioritise and justify their support and care actions. These actions can impact on the health and well-being of patients, their families and the community.

Frontline care: These workers include ambulance and paramedic teams, healthcare support workers, care workers, social workers, medicine, nursing, allied health professionals, activity workers, personal assistants and rehabilitation staff.

Fungal infections: Fungal infections, or mycosis, are diseases caused by fungi (yeast or mould). Fungal infections are most common on the skin or nails, but fungi can also cause infection in the mouth, throat, lungs and many other parts of the body.

Governance: A process used by the health and social care sector to ensure that high quality services and good quality outcomes are offered to all. Care Inspectorate Wales and Healthcare Inspectorate Wales monitor services to make sure everyone who uses the service receives the best care.

Harassment: Harassment is unwanted behaviour that affects the dignity of men and women in the workplace. It may be related to age, sex, race, disability, religion, sexual orientation, nationality or any personal characteristic belonging to that individual. It can be just one event, or a series of events that upset the person and affect their well-being.

Health and Care Professions Council Standards: The Health and Care Professions Council is an organisation that regulates workers in health, psychology and professional care. They set standards, keep a register, ensure quality and investigate complaints. The Health and Care Quality Standards in Wales outline what people can expect when accessing health services and emphasise their role in promoting people's own health and well-being.

Health and Education Improvement Wales (HEIW): Health Education and Improvement Wales (HEIW) is the strategic workforce body for NHS Wales.

Health and Social Care Standards: In 2020 the Health and Social Care (Quality and Engagement) (Wales) Act was passed. The Act had several aims, including strengthening the existing Quality Duty on NHS bodies; imposing a Duty of Honesty on NHS service providers to ensure they are open and honest with patients and service users who are harmed during their care. The Act also strengthened the voice of citizens through the All-Wales Citizen's Voice Body for health and social care.

Health ethics: Health ethics considers moral and ethical values when considering and deciding on health and care issues by health professionals and policy makers. Issues that can impact the health and well-being of patients, families and communities.

Health informatics: An intelligent use of information and technology to provide better patient care.

Healthcare-associated infection (HCAIs): These are associated with the delivery of healthcare services in a healthcare setting that have been caused either by healthcare interventions such as medical or surgical treatment or exposure within the healthcare setting.

Home care workers: Providing care and support to people in their own homes.

Inclusion: An approach in which groups or individuals from different backgrounds are welcomed, culturally and socially accepted, and treated equally.

Individual rights: Enabling the rights of individuals to be upheld in their day-to-day lives.

Infectious condition: This condition includes for example, flu, measles, meningitis (inflammation), MRSA, Mumps, norovirus, tuberculosis (TB), whooping cough.

Infographic: A visual representation of information or data, e.g. such as a chart, diagram or flow diagram.

Injury: Any form of abuse or neglect that can negatively affect that person's well-being.

Intervention: An intervention includes any act that is performed with the aim of improving a person's health. That can include preventing or alleviating illnesses, or by medical action to cure a person or reduce the severity or duration of the disease. It can also include restoring health lost by accident, harm or disease.

Lack of mental capacity: Mental capacity is the ability to make decisions for yourself. People who cannot do this are said to 'lack capacity'. This might be due to illness, injury, a learning disability, or mental health problems that affect the way their brain works.

Legal rights: Legal rights include, for example, the rights of the patient or client and the rights of the workers.

Local and Regional Safeguarding Children Boards: Safeguarding boards that oversee child protection arrangements to facilitate and ensure that all organisations work together to safeguard children and their well-being.

Localised infections: Localised infections are mainly caused by bacteria or virus, where symptoms are confined to one area, e.g. an infected wound.

Maladaptive behaviour: Maladaptive behaviours are actions that prevent people from adapting, adjusting, or participating in different aspects of life. Such actions are intended to help relieve or avoid stress, but they are often disruptive, and may contribute to increased distress, discomfort, and anxiety over time.

Mental capacity: Ability to make a decision, and an ability to evaluate the information, before reaching a rational decision. This ensures that each individual receives the care and support that responds fully to that individual's requirements.

Mobility: Mobility is a patient's ability to move and control their body. Physical mobility requires strength and energy to move the muscles, along with maintaining body stability, and neuromuscular synchronisation. Anything that is disruptive to this process can make it difficult for a person to move or even unable to move at all.

More than words: More than words is the Welsh Government's strategic framework to strengthen Welsh-language services in health and social care. The framework aims to support Welsh speakers to receive services in their first language.

Multi-disciplinary and Multi-agency Teams: Multi-disciplinary and multi-agency working involves appropriately utilising knowledge, skills and best practice from multiple disciplines and across service provider boundaries. They include a group of health and care staff who are members of several organisations and professions (e.g. GPs, social workers, nurses), who work together to make decisions about the treatment of patients, clients and other service users.

Multi-disciplinary team: A multi-disciplinary healthcare team is a group of healthcare professionals from different disciplines who work together to provide holistic, integrated care to a patient. These teams bring together the skills and expertise of each member of the team to enhance patient outcomes.

Negligence: The failure of others to care for the needs of individuals that results in causing harm to that individual. Individuals can also cause harm to

themselves if they fail to take care of themselves, such as by not taking medicine or by not being careful with their diet.

Nervous system: The nervous system maintains internal order within the body by coordinating the activities of muscles and organs, receives input from sense organs, trigger reactions, generating learning and understanding and providing protection from danger. This is primarily conducted through electrochemical signalling between nerves and other cells.

NHS Wales Code of Conduct for Healthcare Support Workers in Wales: The National Code of Conduct for NHS Wales aims to ensure service users and the public receive a consistent, high-quality, safe and effective service from Healthcare Support Workers. The Code focuses on providing effective and compassionate care to the patient or client and to the family as well. This Code of Conduct applies to all Healthcare Support Workers, whether they provide direct or indirect care.

Non-communicable condition: A condition in which infection is not directly transmitted from one person to another.

Nutrition: The food necessary for health and growth and the necessary nutrients for health. A healthy, balanced diet will provide the necessary nutrients.

Nutritional deficiency: Malnutrition means poor nutrition. Most often this is caused by not eating enough (malnutrition), or not eating enough of the right food to give the body the nutrients it needs. Balanced diets should provide enough nutrients, such as calories, protein and vitamins to keep the person healthy. Without this, the person may not get all the nutrients needed, which can lead to malnutrition. This can cause a person to lose weight and vitamin and mineral deficiency – this leaves a person feeling tired, weak and unable to combat disease.

Offensive behaviour: An unwanted behaviour which has the affect of violating a person's dignity, or creating a degrading, humiliating, hostile, intimidating or offensive environment for the person.

Parasitic infections: A parasitic infection attacks the body by using a host for food and shelter. Parasites are organisms that live off other organisms, or hosts, to survive. They can be microscopic or big enough to see with the naked eye. They survive by feeding on the host. Some parasites do not affect the host, while others develop, reproduce or attack the organs that lead to parasitic infection.

Participate: Participate in or become a part of an activity.

Pathogens: These include bacteria, fungi, viruses, protozoa and parasites.

Personal care: Personal care in health and social care is about recognising people as individuals with personal strengths and feelings of how they would like to spend their life. Personal care must therefore be designed to reflect each person's personal needs, preferences and circumstances. To achieve this, it is necessary to create an equal partnership between the individual and the person who provides the care.

Personal plan: A personal care plan is a document that outlines goals, treatment requirements, and care strategies designed for an individual's well-being. The plan is developed collaboratively by a multi-disciplinary team, including healthcare professionals and the individuals themselves. The plan includes both medical and lifestyle preferences.

Physiological condition: A deficiency in the functioning of the organs in the body, and this will cause symptoms which can lead to disease. Different physiological conditions can have a negative impact on people's daily life.

Policies and procedures: Policies describe how an organisation intends to embed and implement its services. The procedures then set out how the health and social care organisation expect their employees to implement their policies and procedures.

Positive approaches: Methods based on principles of care which place the individual at the centre. The aim is to support the well-being of the person by not using negative approaches.

Positive Behaviour Support (PBS): A person centred framework for providing long-term support for people who have, or may be at risk of developing behaviours that challenge.

Prejudice: Bias in health care refers to discriminatory attitudes, behaviours, or practices based on factors such as ethnicity, sexual orientation, gender stereotypes, asylum and migration status, and criminal record. Racial discrimination is a significant problem in health care systems, leading to negative consequences for patients and health care workers, especially black and other non-white people.

Principles of care: Principles of care and core values underpin how health, social care and childcare providers work to ensure that all service users receive the appropriate care. Principles of care ensure that everyone is treated fairly and that they receive the best possible care under the legislation, standards and guidance relevant to the setting or service.

Prion infections: Prion protein that can cause the proteins normally found in the brain to bend in an abnormal way to cause neurodegenerative disease.

Proactive: The ability to create or manage a situation, rather than just react to it after it happens.

Professionalism: The need to respond calmly under difficult circumstances, e.g. when a patient challenges the doctor's decision or opinion.

Protected class: A group of people who are legally protected. It is illegal to discriminate against people on the basis of, e.g. age, gender, disability, race, ethnic background, religion or belief.

Protozoal infections: Protozoal infections are parasitic diseases caused by Protozoal organisms. These organisms are now classified in the supergroups Excavata, Amoebozoa, Harosa (SAR *Supergroup*), and Archaeplastida. Usually, the infection is by contact with an insect or a person touching something that is infected.

Public Health Wales: A body that works to protect and improve health and well-being and reduce health inequalities for the people of Wales. Improvement Cymru is NHS Wales's All Wales Improvement service.

Reasonable adjustment or modifications: Under the Equality Act 2010 public sector organisations must make changes to their working methods or provision to ensure services are accessible to disabled people, as well as everyone else. Reasonable modifications can include modifying buildings by providing a lift, wide doors, ramp and tactile signage, but they can also mean changes to staff policies, procedures and training to ensure that the services are accessible to everyone.

Reflective diary: A reflective diary can be used in a number of ways; whether in a GP practice, in a hospital, on a formal work experience programme, in carrying out a voluntary activity or even an informal discussion with another professional care worker.

Reflective observation: Reflective observation involves observing yourself or observing others before actively analysing those experiences.

Reflective practice: Reflective practice is a process of thinking analytically and critically about your professional practice. It includes drawing upon your experiences and learning from those experiences to improve the quality of care and your practice and procedures. It's a process that needs to be exercised constantly, to learn from each new experience and improve the service you provide for each individual.

Regulator: A body responsible for regulating the service nationally. In Wales, the regulators are Care Inspectorate Wales (CIW) and Healthcare Inspectorate Wales (HIW). They are independent regulators that provide independent and objective assurance on quality, safety and on the effectiveness of healthcare services. They also make recommendations to healthcare providers to promote improvements for the well-being of the people of Wales.

Rehabilitation programme: A rehabilitation programme is a process of assessing, treating and managing a person's physiological condition. It is an opportunity to regain their physical, cognitive, social and psychological condition, as well as enabling the person to enjoy life without the physiological condition. This can include preparing a programme for cardiac rehabilitation, neurological rehabilitation and mobility rehabilitation.

Reliability: Ability to trust a person to perform their tasks in full compliance with the requirements set for carrying out the work.

Reminiscence therapy: An opportunity for patients or clients to recall memories and events from the past.

Memories that will lift their spirits and make them feel better and create an opportunity to socialise by sharing memories with friends.

Residential Care Home: A care setting for individuals who need care and support with everyday activities.

Residential Childcare Worker: Professional codes of conduct and practice provide practice guidance for childcare residential care workers registered with Social Care Wales.

Resilience: Resilience in health and social care is the ability of people or situations to recover quickly after shock or injury, for example. It also includes the ability to maintain personal well-being in the face of challenge.

Respect: The requirement to consider the feelings, rights and wishes of others.

Respiratory system: The respiratory system consists of the set of organs and tissues involved in the uptake of oxygen from the atmosphere, and the release of carbon dioxide generated during aerobic respiration. This gas exchange is also known as breathing.

Responsibilities: Duties and the legal and moral requirements that you must be responsible for as part of your job.

Risk assessment: A method used at work for identifying and recording any risk that has the ability to cause harm. A requirement to determine the level of risk and how to eliminate or reduce that risk.

Risk-taking: Risk-taking involves making decisions that have a level of uncertainty and potential for adverse outcomes. In a care context, this means supporting individuals to make choices about their lives.

Role: Role refers to the position, purpose, or function a health and social care worker has in a particular job, organisation, society, or other specific relationship.

Safeguarding: Safeguarding in health and social care is a system of steps that are taken to protect vulnerable people who are at risk of abuse or neglect.

Self-esteem: The value a person places on themselves or how that person feels about themselves. A person with low self-esteem doesn't feel positive about themselves or their ability to do something.

Self-reflection: Self-reflection in healthcare is a deliberate process that involves thinking clearly, honestly, deeply and critically about different aspects of professional practice. It enables a healthcare professional to improve their practice and improve service delivery.

Sexual health clinic: Clinic for the support, diagnosis and treatment of sexual conditions. Clinics also focus on eliminating the stigma that can belong to sexually transmitted infections (STIs).

Sexual orientation: A person's identity in relation to the sex or gender to which they are sexually attracted, e.g. heterosexual, homosexual.

Social Care Code of Practice for Employers: A list of statements describing the standards expected of social care employers. The focus of the Employers' Code is the standards required by employers to enable their social care workforce to provide a robust, skilful and caring service. The Code is not intended to cover every situation or requirement of an employer's responsibility.

Standards: A description of expectations regarding the requirements of the work. They explain in detail the expectations for delivering the service, and what needs to be done to ensure the quality and the implementation of the legislation. These can include codes of conduct and practice, as well as regulations.

Stigma: Stigma in health and social care refers to those negative attitudes and beliefs people have towards others, based on their health conditions or social circumstances. These can include mental illness, disability, chronic illness, or social issues such as homelessness or substance abuse.

Substance misuse support: Support for a person abusing drugs, as well as introducing management skills to overcome addiction. The aim is to support recovery as an ongoing process.

Support functions: These functions relate to workers working within the health and social care sector who perform support functions. These include, for example: estates and facilities, health informatics, management and administration, finance, human resources, catering, cleaning, porters and information services.

Support services: Support services in healthcare are services that ensure the proper functioning of the organisation, including care delivery, clinical services and revenue management. Support services in care are essential for the proper functioning of hospitals and other health care facilities.

Symptoms: Symptoms are subjective effects of a health problem that are felt or experienced by the person who has the condition. They include sensations like pain and nausea.

Systemic infections: An infection caused mainly by a virus or bacteria spreading through the body's systems, e.g. Sepsis.

Teamwork: Bringing together people with different skills, attitudes and talents to provide the best possible care and treatment to their patients.

Traineeship: A traineeship includes a work experience placement and helps young people prepare for employment or an apprenticeship.

Transmission cycle for infection: An infection transmission cycle consisting of six stages. It is possible however to interrupt this cycle to prevent the transmission of infection. This can be done by replacing or by removing a link or two from the chain, by using Personal Protection Equipment (PPE), or by hand washing, for example.

Value-Based Recruitment (VBR): Value-based recruitment gives organisations the ability to look beyond the usual pool of recruits to find people who may have no previous experience in care but have exactly the right kinds of skills, values and conduct that would make them an asset within any care organisation.

Viral infections: Viral infections are any illness you get from a virus (a small germ that uses your cells to reproduce). Common viral illnesses include colds, influenza, COVID-19, norovirus ("stomach flu") and herpes simplex virus (cold sores). Several viruses go away on their own, but some cause life-threatening illnesses or lead to chronic illness.

Visual signs: People may use the words 'sign' and 'symptom' interchangeably. However, a symptom is something an individual experiences, while a sign is something a doctor, or other person, notices. People may confuse signs and symptoms, but there are important differences that affect their use in the field of medicine. Any objective evidence of a disease, such as a skin rash or a cough, is a sign. A doctor, family member, and the individual experiencing the signs can identify these. Something others may see, such as a bruise, soreness or losing or gaining weight . These can also include changes in behaviour and mood.

Well-being: Good health, feeling good, happiness and the ability to do things and enjoy life.

Welsh NHS Confederation: The Welsh NHS Confederation represents the Local Health Boards, three NHS Trusts and two Health Authorities.

Whistleblowing: An individual discloses information that is considered by them to be unlawful or harmful to the patient or client, and that they need to disclose that information to senior members of staff or to the authorities.

Worker: An individual who provides care, support or service to a patient or client.

Workplace: A setting that provides care and support, such as residential childcare, at an individuals' own home, foster care.

Index

Image credits

The authors and publishers would like to thank the following for their permission to use copyright material included within this book: